Digital Signals, Processors

TW

D1579016

98

}8

9

28

13 J

L.

Accessior

LUTON COLLEGE OF
HIGHER EDUCATION
PARK SQ LIBRARY

3400827686

621.38043

LyN

Macmillan New Electronics Series
Series Editor: Paul A. Lynn

Rodney F. W. Coates, *Underwater Acoustic Systems*
W. Forsythe and R. M. Goodall, *Digital Control*
C. G. Guy, *Data Communications for Engineers*
Paul A. Lynn, *Digital Signals, Processors and Noise*
Paul A. Lynn, *Radar Systems*
A. F. Murray and H. M. Reekie, *Integrated Circuit Design*
F. J. Owens, *Signal Processing of Speech*
Dennis N. Pim, *Television and Teletext*
M. J. N. Sibley, *Optical Communications*
Martin S. Smith, *Introduction to Antennas*
P. M. Taylor, *Robotic Control*
G. S. Virk, *Digital Computer Control Systems*
Allan Waters, *Active Filter Design*

Series Standing Order

If you would like to receive further titles in this series as they are published, you can make use of our standing order facility. To place a standing order please contact your bookseller or, in case of difficulty, write to us at the address below with your name and address and the name of the series. Please state with which title you wish to begin your standing order. (If you live outside the United Kingdom we may not have the rights for your area, in which case we will forward your order to the publisher concerned.)

Customer Services Department, Macmillan Distribution Ltd
Houndmills, Basingstoke, Hampshire, RG21 2XS, England.

Digital Signals, Processors and Noise

Paul A. Lynn

BSc(Eng), ACGI, PhD, MIEE

Macmillan New Electronics
Introductions to Advanced Topics

MACMILLAN

© Paul A. Lynn 1992

All rights reserved. No reproduction, copy or transmission
of this publication may be made without written permission.

No paragraph of this publication may be reproduced, copied
or transmitted save with written permission or in accordance
with the provisions of the Copyright, Designs and Patents Act
1988 or under the terms of any licence permitting limited
copying issued by the Copyright Licensing Agency,
90 Tottenham Court Road, London W1P 9HE.

Any person who does any unauthorised act in relation to
this publication may be liable to criminal prosecution and
civil claims for damages.

First edition 1992

Published by
THE MACMILLAN PRESS LTD
Houndmills, Basingstoke, Hampshire RG21 2XS
and London
Companies and representatives
throughout the world

Printed in Hong Kong
Typeset by TecSet Ltd, Wallington, Surrey.

ISBN 0–333–54586–9
ISBN 0–333–54587–7 Pbk

A catalogue record for this book is
available from the British Library

Contents

Series Editor's Foreword

The rapid development of electronics and its engineering applications ensures that new topics are always competing for a place in university and polytechnic courses. But it is often difficult for lecturers to find suitable books for recommendation to students, particularly when a topic is covered by a short lecture module, or as an 'option'.

This Series offers introductions to advanced topics. The level is generally that of second and subsequent years of undergraduate courses in electronic and electrical engineering, computer science and physics. Some of the authors will paint with a broad brush; others will concentrate on a narrower topic, and cover it in greater detail. But in all cases the titles in the Series will provide a sound basis for further reading of the specialist literature, and an up-to-date appreciation of practical applications and likely trends.

The level, scope and approach of the Series should also appeal to practising engineers and scientists encountering an area of electronics for the first time, or needing a rapid and authoritative update.

Paul A. Lynn

Preface

In putting together this short text on Digital Signal Processing (DSP), I have had three main objectives. Firstly, I wanted to provide undergraduate students – as well as postgraduates and practising engineers needing an introduction to the field – with a concise and accessible account of the theoretical background to DSP and its practical applications. Secondly, since it is now commonplace for the individual to own (or have ready access to) a personal computer, I decided to illustrate key DSP topics and design methods with computer programs. And finally, knowing that most newcomers to DSP find the topic of digital noise, and signals in noise, especially difficult, I have included introductory chapters on the description and processing of random sequences.

Some of these objectives perhaps deserve a little more explanation. As far as the computer programs are concerned, I feel sure that there is a great deal to be gained, in both confidence and understanding, by using and modifying DSP programs on a general-purpose computer, and by seeing the results of digital processing build up on a computer screen. A large number of figures in the text have been produced in this way, and I hope that many of my readers will have the chance to reproduce the graphical outputs, and experiment with further programs of their own. Incidentally, quite a number of the figures have previously been used in my book *Introductory Digital Signal Processing with Computer Applications*, co-authored with Wolfgang Fuerst and published by Wiley in 1989, and I am grateful for the publisher's agreement to include them. The programs are listed in both BASIC and PASCAL in Appendix A, and although they cannot do more than indicate some of the possibilities of this approach to teaching and learning DSP, I hope they will be found useful.

As far as noise, and signals in noise, are concerned, many years of teaching these topics (in both analog and digital versions) convinced me that an approach with copious illustrations should be attractive to students and allow them to visualise the essential mathematical background. The mathematics itself I have kept as simple as possible, consistent with the need for accuracy; and I have tried, at every stage, to illustrate the main theoretical results by involving the reader in the actual business of processing random digital signals and noise sequences on a digital computer.

Of course, any book of this length on a huge subject must be selective. I decided early on that it would be sensible to cover the basic theory of linear DSP and its application using general-purpose computers reasonably thoroughly, but omit any material on hardware or VLSI aspects. The result is inevitably a compromise, but one which I trust will appeal across a wide range of engineering and scientific disciplines, especially to those who need an accessible introduction without getting involved, so to speak, in the nuts and bolts of the subject.

Paul A. Lynn
Bristol, 1992

1 Introduction

1.1 Background

Until about 1970 Digital Signal Processing (DSP) was considered something of a curiosity by most engineers and scientists – if indeed they had heard of it at all. Then, throughout the next decade, and thanks to the dramatic development of digital computers, there was an enormous growth of interest in both its theoretical and practical aspects. Equally dramatic advances in VLSI technology in the 1980s made it possible to design DSP devices on a single chip of silicon. Today, a wide range of implementations is possible – from software processors realised on general-purpose computers or microprocessors right through to fast, application-specific, hardware. DSP already has an established role in fields as diverse as electronic engineering, biomedicine, process control, seismology, aerospace and data processing; and there is every sign that the list will continue to grow.

DSP algorithms, which include the very important class of processors known as *digital filters*, achieve their effects by numerical operations on sampled signals and data. Broadly speaking, they mirror the continuous-time (analog) circuits which have been used by electronic and communication engineers ever since the early days of radio. However, as we shall see, the digital domain offers certain technical possibilities denied to the analog circuit designer, plus the practical advantages of reliability and stability. Furthermore, when a digital processor is programmed on a computer or microprocessor, it is normally a straightforward matter to adjust its characteristics by changing the software.

DSP is a large and expanding field, and in a short book we cannot do more than introduce some of its main features. In chapters 1–3 we develop the basic theoretical background to the subject, as applied to deterministic signals in the time and frequency domains. In chapters 4 and 5 we extend the discussion to random signals and sequences, developing ideas which are central to both signal processing and communications. Throughout, key concepts and design methods are illustrated with the aid of computer programs. These are listed in both BASIC and PASCAL in appendix A, and are suitable for most general-purpose computers, including personal

1

computers. It is hoped that many of our readers will have the opportunity to try them out for themselves.

By the time you have read and studied this book, you should therefore have a basic understanding of the theoretical background to modern DSP, and its software implementation. However, one proviso is in order: we will concentrate on linear DSP algorithms, which obey the *Principle of Superposition*. Non-linear techniques are certainly important, but their theoretical treatment is beyond the scope of an introductory book. Fortunately linear DSP has found extensive practical application, and forms a satisfying body of knowledge with many links to continuous-time signal and system theory.

We now illustrate two practical applications of linear DSP taken from very different fields. Our aim is to provide motivation for the theoretical work which follows; it is not necessary for you to understand all the details at this stage.

The first illustration concerns the use of a simple *low-pass digital filter* to smooth stock market or financial data. Figure 1.1 shows fluctuations in the share price of *DSP International Inc.* between 1988 and 1990. The heavy, rapidly fluctuating, curve represents the price recorded day by day. There are more than 1000 values (or samples) altogether, so for convenience we have joined them together to give a continuous curve.

It is often helpful to smooth such 'raw data', revealing underlying trends. A widely-used technique is to estimate a *moving-average*. Each smoothed value is computed as the average of a number of preceding raw-data values, and the process is repeated sample-by-sample through the record.

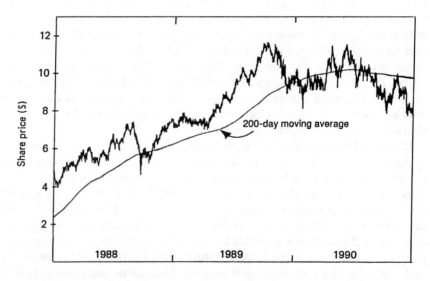

Figure 1.1   Share price, *DSP International Inc.*, 1988–90

The figure shows the 200-day moving-average (with individual values again joined together for convenience). 200-day averages are popular with financial analysts for investigating long-term trends. Clearly, such processing gives a pronounced smoothing, or low-pass filtering, action.

From the DSP point of view, the daily share price provides samples of an input signal $x[n]$. The smoothed values represent output samples $y[n]$ from the moving-average process. The 200-day average may be computed using the algorithm:

$$y[n] = \{x[n] + x[n-1] + x[n-2] + \ldots x[n-199]\}/200$$

$$= 0.005 \sum_{k=0}^{199} x[n-k] \tag{1.1}$$

It is a simple matter to enter the raw data in a computer, and to write a program for calculating the output $y[n]$. Every time a new value of x becomes available, we can produce a new value of y.

Equation (1.1) is a *recurrence formula*, which is used over and over again to find successive output samples $y[n]$. It is also called a *difference equation*. It is *non-recursive*, because each output value is computed solely from input values (rather than previous outputs). And the equation defines a simple low-pass digital filter. Much of DSP is concerned with the design and use of digital filters, which can be tailored to give a wide variety of processing functions.

You may have noticed that the above moving-average algorithm is not very efficient. The computation of each output value is almost exactly the same as the one before it, except that the most recent input sample is included, and the most distant one is discarded. Using this idea, we can generate a much more efficient algorithm. Equation (1.1) shows that the next smoothed output value must be

$$y[n+1] = 0.005\{x[n+1] + x[n] + x[n-1] + \ldots x[n-198]\}$$

$$= y[n] + 0.005\{x[n+1] - x[n-199]\}$$

Since this is a recurrence formula which applies for any value of n, we may subtract 1 from each term in square brackets, giving

$$y[n] = y[n-1] + 0.005\{x[n] - x[n-200]\} \tag{1.2}$$

Equation (1.2) confirms that we can estimate each output sample by *updating the previous output* $y[n-1]$. The equation defines a recursive version of the filter which is much more efficient, requiring far fewer additions/subtractions. Note that equations (1.1) and (1.2) are equivalent from the signal processing point of view.

Smoothing, or low-pass, filters are widely used in DSP. In fact there are many different types of design, and the simple moving-average algorithm we have described would not be suitable for most applications.

Figure 1.2 summarises the type of situation we are considering: $x[n]$ is the sampled input signal to a digital signal processor, and $y[n]$ is the sampled output. Successive signal values may be thought of as regularly-spaced samples of underlying analog waveforms, and are separated from one another by the system sampling interval T. The integer variable n denotes the sample number, with $n = 0$ corresponding to some convenient time origin or reference. In effect we may regard $x[n]$ and $y[n]$ as sequences of numerical data which are binary-coded for the purposes of signal processing. It is worth noting that they are not necessarily time functions; for example they may be functions of distance. However, for convenience we generally assume that n is a time variable.

Our second practical DSP illustration is taken from the field of biomedicine. In figure 1.3, part (a) shows an *electromyogram (EMG)* signal representing electrical activity in a muscle. Such signals are often recorded in medical clinics and laboratories, and are readily picked up by electrodes placed on the surface of the skin. They may be used to indicate muscle function in health and disease, and for the automatic control of artificial limbs. Since they represent superposed statistical activity in many individual muscle fibres, they are essentially random in nature. Typically, their spectra peak at around 60 Hz, with significant energy between about 20 and 600 Hz; sampling rates of around 2 kHz are commonly used.

In part (b) of the figure, the EMG is severely contaminated by sinusoidal interference at mains supply frequency (50 Hz in Europe, 60 Hz in the USA). This is quite a common problem when recording biomedical signals, owing to pick-up in electrode leads. It must obviously be reduced if the signal is to have diagnostic value. Since such signals are often stored in computers, we have the opportunity to reduce the interference using a digital filter.

Before describing a suitable DSP algorithm, we should explain the form of the sampled signals in the figure. They have been drawn by computer,

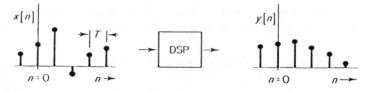

Figure 1.2   Input and output signals of a digital signal processor

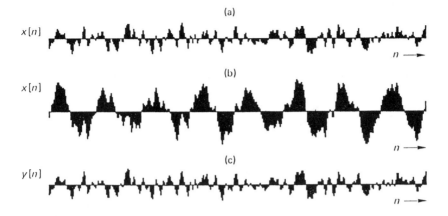

Figure 1.3   Removing mains-frequency interference from an electromyogram (*abscissa: 320 samples*)

and each sample value is represented by a thin vertical bar. In this case there are 320 sample values across the page, and the vertical bars are contiguous. This gives the plots their solid appearance. You will meet many examples of such computer plots later, and will have the opportunity to reproduce some of them for yourself on a personal computer.

The digital filter we require in this case should have a *bandstop*, or *notch*, characteristic, which rejects a narrow band of frequencies centred at mains supply frequency. The following difference equation is suitable:

$$y[n] = 1.9556y[n-1] - 0.9801y[n-2] + x[n] - 1.9754x[n-1]$$
$$+ x[n-2] \tag{1.3}$$

Part (c) of the figure shows the dramatic effect of this recursive filter on the contaminated signal of part (b). If you look carefully, you will see that the interference has been greatly reduced, without significantly distorting the signal waveform.

At this stage we certainly do not expect you to understand how equation (1.3) has been derived. The illustration is intended to whet the appetite for some DSP theory in later chapters! However we should just add that a digital filter algorithm is always designed for a particular *sampling rate*. If the interference is at 50 Hz, this algorithm is effective at a sampling rate of 2 kHz; if it is at 60 Hz, the appropriate sampling rate is 2.4 kHz.

Once again, it is a straightforward matter to program such a filter on a general-purpose computer, by including equation (1.3) in a program loop. The raw data, represented by part (b) of the figure, is loaded into an array *x*, and the filtered output generated in an array *y*.

What types of DSP system would be needed in the foregoing applications? In the case of the stock market data of figure 1.1, the input signal is only sampled once per day, so even the slowest computer or digital processor would be more than adequate for calculating the smoothed output. Indeed, one could very easily perform the required calculation on the back of an envelope, and still have plenty of time left over! The EMG in figure 1.3 is rather more demanding since the sampling frequency required is about 2 kHz. If the digital notch filter is to operate in real time, the calculations defined by equation (1.3) must be performed in about half a millisecond. This is probably marginal for the present generation of small computers (including personal computers), so we are close to requiring a faster processor. Clearly, as sampling rates increase and filter algorithms become more complicated, the problem worsens. And by the time we get to sampling rates of, say, 100 kHz and above, real-time processing is likely to demand special digital hardware tailored to the particular application.

1.2 Sampling and analog-to-digital conversion

An overall DSP scheme is shown in figure 1.4. The analog input signal might represent variations in a voltage, temperature, pressure, light intensity – or the EMG already illustrated in figure 1.3. If the signal is not inherently electrical, it is first converted to a proportional voltage fluctuatin by a suitable transducer. Notice that the first stage in the processing chain is very often an analog low-pass filter, known as an *anti-aliasing* filter, which is designed to limit the frequency range of the signal prior to sampling. The reasons for this will become clear a little later.

The signal is next sampled and converted into a binary code by an *analog-to-digital converter (ADC)*. After digital signal processing it may be changed back into analog form using a *digital-to-analog converter (DAC)*. This normally gives an output of the *zero-order-hold* type, in which each sample value is held steady over one complete sampling interval. The resulting staircase waveform may be smoothed by a final low-pass analog filter to remove its sharp transitions.

There are several variations on the above theme. For example, after DSP the signal may be used to drive a computer display (as in figure 1.3), or it may be transmitted in binary form to a remote terminal. In data processing applications (such as that shown in figure 1.1) the numerical

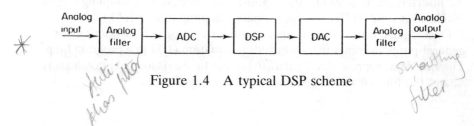

Figure 1.4   A typical DSP scheme

data representing the input signal may be available on a computer disk, or it may be entered on a keyboard by a computer operator. In such cases sampling and analog-to-digital conversion is an inherent part of the data entry process. Similarly, a computer print-out of processed data values may take the place of digital-to-analog conversion.

How fast should an analog input signal be sampled? Clearly, if we sample too infrequently we are likely to lose the faster fluctuations (and hence the higher frequency components); but if we sample too often, we find ourselves having to store and process an unnecessarily large number of numerical values. We must therefore choose some intermediate sampling rate which is adequate, without being excessive.

The answer to this important question is provided by Shannon's famous *Sampling Theorem*, which may be stated as follows:

An analog signal containing components up to some maximum frequency f_1 Hz may be completely represented by regularly-spaced samples, provided the sampling rate is at least $2f_1$ samples per second.

Thus a speech waveform having components up to $f_1 = 3$ kHz should be sampled at least 6000 times per second. A television signal with $f_1 = 5$ MHz should be sampled at least 10 million times per second – and so on.

Although we do not have space for a formal proof of the Sampling Theorem, the reasoning behind it is illustrated in figure 1.5. Part (a) shows the magnitude spectrum of a typical analog signal prior to sampling. Its precise shape is unimportant; what matters is that there are no components above some maximum frequency f_1 – here taken as 3 kHz. It may be shown that sampling causes the original spectrum to repeat around multiples of the sampling frequency. This is illustrated in part (b) of the figure for a sampling frequency of 8 kHz. We may think of the spectral repetitions, which in theory extend to infinitely high frequencies, as a consequence of representing a smooth analog waveform by a set of narrow samples, or *impulses*.

In principle we could recover the spectrum shown in part (a) – and hence the original analog signal – using a low-pass filter. Such a *reconstituting filter* should transmit equally all components up to 3 kHz, but reject the spectral repetitions caused by sampling. Indeed this would still just be possible if we sampled at 6 kHz, as shown in part (c) of the figure, providing we had an 'ideal' reconstituting filter with an infinitely sharp cut off (labelled 'A'). Note that 6 kHz is the minimum allowable sampling frequency according to the Sampling Theorem. However if we fail to obey it – say by reducing the sampling frequency to 5 kHz as in part (d) – we get overlap between successive spectral repetitions (labelled 'B'). The effect,

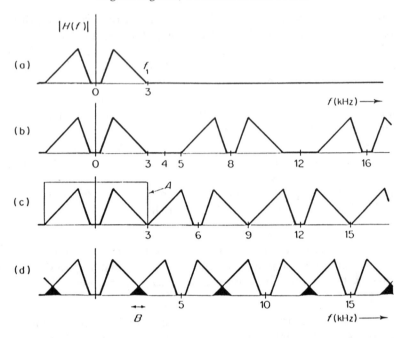

Figure 1.5   The effects of sampling on a signal spectrum

known as *aliasing*, corrupts the original spectrum, which cannot now be recovered. Information has been lost through inadequate sampling.

It is normal practice to sample rather faster than demanded by the Sampling Theorem. This introduces a guardband between successive spectral repetitions (for example, the range 3–5 kHz in part (b) of the figure), and gives a safety margin. Also, we often use a low-pass anti-aliasing filter on the input side (as in figure 1.4), to ensure that the maximum frequency f_1 is not, in fact, exceeded.

Sampling and binary coding of an analog signal is normally carried out by an analog-to-digital converter (ADC). The process is illustrated in figure 1.6. For simplicity we have assumed a 3-bit binary code, giving just eight discrete amplitude 'slots'. Note how each sample value falls within one of these slots, and is allocated the corresponding code. The process inevitably introduces small errors, known as *quantisation* errors. Since they are usually more or less random, we can regard them as unwanted noise introduced by the coding process. Clearly, it can be reduced by using a longer binary code, and by trying to ensure that the analog signal fills the available amplitude range of the ADC.

Once introduced, however, quantisation noise cannot be removed. This may appear to be a serious drawback of digital processing. Remember, however, that any analog signal has a certain amount of noise or

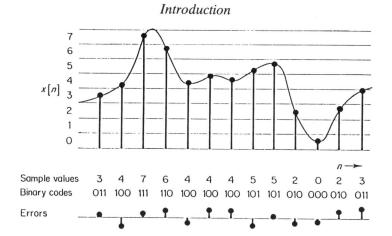

Figure 1.6   Converting an analog signal into a binary code

uncertainty associated with it anyway. So quantisation need not cause significant further degradation provided a long enough binary code is chosen. Typically, DSP schemes use code lengths between 8 and 16 bits.

In addition to input quantisation effects, DSP algorithms generally introduce a certain amount of computational error. Essentially this is because a finite wordlength is used to represent coefficients and numerical results within the machine. The effects are unlikely to be troublesome when working in high-level languages on general-purpose computers, and we do not consider them further in this book. However if you become a specialist designer of fast DSP hardware, you will have to take them very much into account.

1.3   Time-domain analysis

1.3.1   Describing signals and processors

Our next task is to describe some basic types of digital signal – impulses, steps, exponentials and sinusoids. There are two main, interrelated, reasons why such signals are of great value in DSP. Firstly, complicated real-life signals such as those previously illustrated in figures 1.1 and 1.3 may generally be considered as the summation of a number of simpler, basic, signals. And secondly, if we can define the response of a linear processor to basic signals, we can predict its response to more complicated ones.

Figure 1.7 shows the unit impulse function $\delta[n]$, and the unit step function $u[n]$. They are defined as:

Digital Signals, Processors and Noise

Figure 1.7 Basic digital signals: (a) the unit impulse function, and (b) the unit step function

$$\delta[n] = 0, n \neq 0 \qquad \text{and} \qquad u[n] = 0, n < 0$$
$$= 1, n = 0 \qquad\qquad\qquad = 1, n \geq 0 \qquad\qquad (1.4)$$

As we shall see, the unit impulse is of the greatest significance in DSP theory and practice. Note that it is the *first-order difference* of $u[n]$; conversely, $u[n]$ is the *running sum* of $\delta[n]$. Thus

$$\delta[n] = u[n] - u[n - 1] \qquad\qquad (1.5)$$

and

$$u[n] = \sum_{m=-\infty}^{n} \delta[m] \qquad\qquad (1.6)$$

We next consider exponential and sinusoidal signals. Part (a) of figure 1.8 shows a function of the form.

$$x[n] = A \exp(bn) \qquad\qquad (1.7)$$

where $b < 0$. This is a decaying real exponential, in which successive sample values follow a simple geometric progression. Such functions are theoretically eternal – they continue for ever in both directions. In practice, however, we generally work with signals which are zero prior to some reference instant, normally taken as $n = 0$. Such an exponential may conveniently be written as

$$x[n] = A \exp(bn) u[n] \qquad\qquad (1.8)$$

In other words it is 'switched on' at $n = 0$ by being multiplied, or *modulated*, by the unit step function.

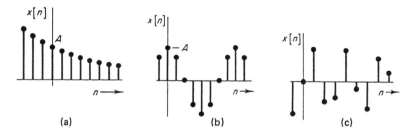

Figure 1.8   Basic digital signals: exponentials and sinusoids

Digital sines and cosines may be written in the form

$$x[n] = A \sin(n\Omega) \quad \text{and} \quad x[n] = A \cos(n\Omega) \tag{1.9}$$

where A is the amplitude, n is the usual integer variable and Ω is the frequency. Actually although we refer to it as a 'frequency', we should remember that since n is dimensionless, Ω must be expressed in radians rather than radians per second. This is one difference between digital sinusoids and their analog counterparts. Part (b) of figure 1.8 shows a digital cosinusoid for which $\Omega = \pi/4$.

Another difference is that digital sines and cosines are not necessarily periodic. Although the sample values lie on a periodic *envelope*, their numerical values may not form a repetitive sequence. Part (c) of the figure illustrates this for a sine. It is hard to tell merely by inspection whether the signal is sinusoidal or not. Intuitively it is fairly obvious that such a function will only be periodic if the sampling interval bears a simple relationship to the period of the underlying analog waveform. Formally, this condition is met if

$$\Omega = 2\pi(m/N) \tag{1.10}$$

where m and N are integers.

As already noted, equation (1.9) defines digital sines and cosines in terms of the integer variable n and a dimensionless frequency variable Ω expressed in radians. If we write $\Omega = \omega T$, where ω is the usual angular frequency in radians per second and T is the sampling interval, we obtain

$$x[n] = A \sin(n\Omega) = A \sin(n\omega T) = A \sin(2\pi nf/f_s) \tag{1.11}$$

where f_s is the sampling frequency. Our sampled sinusoid has been redefined in terms of frequency in hertz, and time in seconds.

A third and very significant difference between analog and digital sinusoids is that the digital ones are, in an important sense, ambiguous. This is illustrated by figure 1.9, in which we show two sampled sinusoids with exactly the same sample values. In fact there is an infinite set of such waveforms, and a sampled sinusoid of frequency Ω is identical to those of frequency $\Omega + 2\pi$, $\Omega + 4\pi$, $\Omega + 6\pi$, and so on.

Such ambiguity is directly related to our discussion of the Sampling Theorem in the previous section. We saw that when an analog signal is sampled, its spectrum is repeated around multiples of the sampling frequency. This may be seen as a consequence of representing a continuous waveform by a set of instantaneous samples, or impulses. An alternative view is that a digital signal has a whole set of possible spectral representations, separated from one another by 2π along the frequency axis. Since all are equally valid, all must appear in a spectral diagram.

We now turn our attention to some general aspects of digital processors. As already noted, we are restricting ourselves in this book to *linear* algorithms which obey the Principle of Superposition. This has the great advantage that responses to a unit impulse, or a set of sinusoidal frequencies, give fundamental descriptions of a processor in the time and frequency domains respectively – very much as they do with linear analog systems.

Other properties we shall generally assume in this book are *time-invariance, causality* and *stability*. By *time invariance*, we mean that a processor's characteristics are unaffected by time origin; we are therefore excluding adaptive systems. *Causality* implies that an output signal depends only on present and previous values of the input. You might assume that practical signal processors are always causal, because they can hardly anticipate the future. However if we record a signal or data and subsequently process it by computer, the software need not be causal (of course it is reasonable to object that the complete recording/processing system *is* causal; but at this point we risk becoming entangled in semantics).

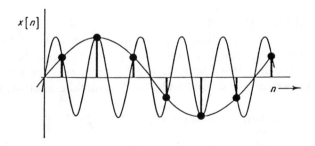

Figure 1.9   Ambiguity in digital sinusoids

Stability implies that a processor produces a finite, or *bounded*, output in response to a bounded input. This means that if it is disturbed from its resting state by an input signal such as a unit impulse, then its output must sooner or later settle to zero. Useful signal processors are invariably stable.

Processors which are linear and time-invariant (LTI) involve the following types of operation on the sample values of an input signal (and on previous outputs in the case of recursive processors):

storage/delay
addition/subtraction
multiplication by constants

As an example, consider the digital notch filter illustrated in figure 1.3. Equation (1.3) gave its difference equation as

$$y[n] = 1.9556y[n - 1] - 0.9801y[n - 2] + x[n] - 1.9754x[n - 1] + x[n - 2] \tag{1.12}$$

Although we are not yet in a position to explain how the filter works, the equation shows that it requires only the above types of operation. We may safely conclude that the filter is an LTI processor.

To conclude this section, we show how a digital filter can be represented in block diagram form. Figure 1.10 arranges the above difference equation as a series of blocks producing time delay (by one sampling interval T), multiplication by coefficients, and addition. Note that the filter has a non-recursive part and a recursive part; and that the recursive part involves feedback. We should just add that digital filters and processors can, in general, be realised using a variety of different structures. This may be an important consideration when designing special-purpose hardware.

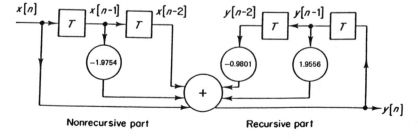

Figure 1.10 Block diagram of a digital filter

1.3.2 Digital convolution

In this section we describe one of the most important of all DSP operations – digital convolution. It allows us to find the output signal from any LTI processor in response to any input signal. It also gives valuable insights into the ways in which trains of signal samples are modified by linear processing.

The output $y[n]$ from a processor may be obtained by *convolving* the input signal with a second time function representing the processor itself. This second function is the processor's *impulse response*. The convolution takes place entirely in the time domain, without any need to consider the frequency spectrum of the input signal, or the frequency response of the processor.

Convolution may sound complicated, but is in fact no more than a form of superposition. It relies upon the fact that any input signal can be represented by a series of weighted, time-shifted, unit impulses. Since an LTI processor obeys the Principle of Superposition, the output signal must equal the summation of its responses to all such impulses, considered separately.

Before we can describe convolution in detail, we must therefore develop two subsidiary themes. First, we must be able to characterise any input signal as a set of impulse functions; second, we need to consider how a digital processor responds to an individual impulse.

In general, an input signal may be written in the form:

$$x[n] = \ldots + x[-2]\delta[n + 2] + x[-1]\delta[n + 1] + x[0]\delta[n]$$
$$+ x[1]\delta[n - 1] + x[2]\delta[n - 2] + \ldots \tag{1.13}$$

Thus we are allowing the signal to exist over all time, and representing each of its sample values as a weighted, shifted, unit impulse. For example, the sample occurring at $n = 1$, which has the numerical value $x[1]$, is given by $x[1]\delta[n - 1]$. Equation (1.13) may be written in compact form as

$$x[n] = \sum_{k=-\infty}^{\infty} x[k]\delta[n - k] \tag{1.14}$$

Since the integer k takes on all values between $\pm\infty$, $x[n]$ is a completely general signal. Of course, if we know that it is zero prior to $n = 0$, we can limit k to the range 0 to ∞, and so on.

Let us now consider the response of a LTI processor to a unit impulse. Note first that if we deliver such a signal to the input, the 'excitation' is confined to the instant $n = 0$. Any subsequent output signal must be *characteristic of the processor itself*, since the input signal has ceased. This is why the impulse response is such a fundamental property of a linear processor.

The impulse response is usually given the symbol $h[n]$. If the input to a processor is $\delta[n]$, the output must be $h[n]$. This is illustrated by figure 1.11. Impulse responses can take on a wide variety of forms, depending on the processing action they represent. Note, however, that the impulse response of a causal, stable, processor cannot begin before $n = 0$, and it must eventually decay to zero.

It is straightforward to evaluate a processor's impulse response if we know its difference equation. Take, for example, the digital notch filter previously illustrated in figure 1.3, with a difference equation given by equation (1.3). If $x[n]$ becomes $\delta[n]$ then the output signal is, by definition, $h[n]$. Hence we may write

$$h[n] = 1.9556h[n - 1] - 0.9801h[n - 2] + \delta[n] - 1.9754\delta[n - 1]$$
$$+ \delta[n - 2] \tag{1.15}$$

Figure 1.12 illustrates the form of $h[n]$, which has been evaluated term-by-term on a computer using equation (1.15). Note that the term $\delta[n]$ only contributes at $n = 0$, $\delta[n - 1]$ only contributes at $n = 1$, and $\delta[n - 2]$ at $n = 2$. The impulse response certainly continues beyond $n = 2$, but is generated recursively, without any further contributions from the input. We cannot easily explain the precise form of $h[n]$ at this stage; but we see that it

Figure 1.11 The impulse response of an LTI processor

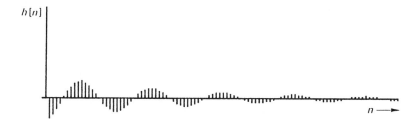

Figure 1.12 Computed impulse response of a notch filter

begins at $n = 0$, and decays towards zero as n increases. Therefore the filter is both causal and stable, as expected.

We are now in a position to define the process of digital convolution. In equation (1.14) we expressed an input signal as a set of weighted, shifted, impulses. Each of these impulses must produce a similarly weighted and shifted version of the impulse response at the processor's output. Since the processor obeys the Principle of Superposition, the total output equals the summation of all the responses. Hence if we replace $\delta[n - k]$ in equation (1.14) by $h[n - k]$, we obtain an expression for the output signal $y[n]$:

$$y[n] = \sum_{k=-\infty}^{\infty} x[k]h[n - k] \tag{1.16}$$

This very important equation is known as the *convolution sum*. It tells us how to calculate the output signal from an LTI processor in response to any input signal, given the processor's impulse response. In fact the convolution sum occurs in two slightly different forms, and it will be helpful for our future work to develop the alternative form straight away. If we write $m = n - k$, so that $k = n - m$, equation (1.16) becomes

$$y[n] = \sum_{m=\infty}^{-\infty} x[n - m]h[m] = \sum_{k=-\infty}^{\infty} x[n - k]h[k] \tag{1.17}$$

Note that equations (1.16) and (1.17) are identical, except that x and h are interchanged. From now on, we will use the latter form.

Equation (1.17) has a very convenient and useful graphical interpretation. To illustrate this, suppose we have the input signal and impulse response shown in figure 1.13, and that we wish to calculate the output sample value $y[1]$. Equation (1.17) shows that it is given by

$$y[1] = \sum_{k=-\infty}^{\infty} x[1 - k]h[k] \tag{1.18}$$

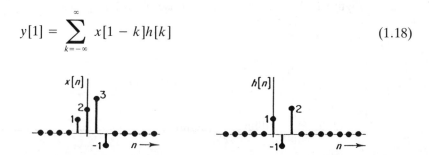

Figure 1.13   Input signal and impulse response of a simple processor

We now interpret the variable k as time *measured back into the past* from the instant for which we wish to calculate the output – in this case $n = 1$. The term $h[k]$ in equation (1.18) is therefore represented by a *time-reversed version* of the impulse response, as shown in figure 1.14, and $x[1 - k]$ is simply the input signal. Finally we multiply the two functions and sum all finite products to give the output value $y[1]$, as indicated by equation (1.18). In this case the figure shows that

$$y[1] = (1 \times 2) + (2 \times -1) + (3 \times 1) = 3$$

To find the next output value $y[2]$, we move the reversed impulse response forward one sampling interval, and repeat the multiplication and summation process. It is quite straightforward to show that the complete output signal sequence in this case is

$$1, 1, 3, 0, 7, -2, 0, 0, 0, \ldots$$

with the first value occurring at $n = 0$. You may like to check this for yourself.

In normal English usage, the word 'convolution' means a kind of 'coiling or twisting'. In the graphical technique just described the impulse response is first time-reversed, then shifted along in a series of steps. At each step it is multiplied by the input signal, and all finite products are summed. You may or may not feel that this sequence of events is tantamount to a 'coiling

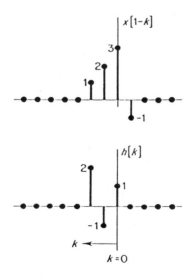

Figure 1.14   Graphical interpretation of convolution

or twisting' – perhaps a 'rolling together' of the two functions would be a more accurate description.

Valuable though the graphical technique is for visualising the process of convolution, we can hardly use it for lengthy signals or impulse responses. In such cases it is clearly sensible to get a computer to do the work for us, using equation (1.17). The first of the programs listed in appendix A (in BASIC and PASCAL) is a general-purpose digital convolution program which can work with any form of input signal and impulse response. Input and output signals are normalised to the same peak value before plotting on the screen. (This means that the vertical scales of the plots have no particular significance.) The input signal is loaded into array X, starting at location 60. The impulse response $h[n]$ is assumed causal, and should have less than 60 terms. The program loads $h[n]$ into array H, then implements the convolution sum directly.

You may like to use the program to explore various aspects of digital convolution. Here, we demonstrate once again the action of a simple moving-average low-pass filter (see also figure 1.1). Figure 1.15 shows the screen plot for an input signal containing two distinct sinusoidal components:

$$x[n] = \sin(2\pi n/60) + \sin(2\pi n/10), \quad 60 \leqslant n \leqslant 320 \tag{1.19}$$

processed by the 10-point moving-average filter:

$$h[n] = 0.1, \quad 0 \leqslant n \leqslant 9$$

$$= 0 \quad \text{elsewhere} \tag{1.20}$$

(Recalling the graphical interpretation of convolution, we see that this form of $h[n]$ will multiply 10 successive input samples by 0.1, before summation to give a single output value. It therefore performs a moving-average over 10 points. The program listings in appendix A include the above choices for $x[n]$ and $h[n]$.)

The form of $y[n]$ clearly demonstrates the low-pass action of this type of filter. The lower of the two frequencies in $x[n]$, with 60 samples per period, is transmitted. The higher one, with 10 samples per period, is not. In fact we have chosen a rather special case, in which the higher frequency is completely suppressed. The reason is quite straightforward. The filter averages over 10 input sample values, so it eliminates a frequency component with exactly 10 samples per period. More generally we would expect such a filter to reduce high frequencies without eliminating them completely.

You have probably noticed the rather curious transient which occurs at the start of $y[n]$. This 'start-up' effect is due to the sudden application of

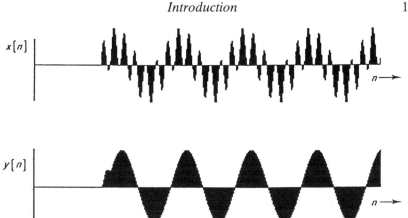

Figure 1.15 A moving-average filter applied to an input signal with two distinct frequency components (*abscissa: 320 samples*)

the input, and has a duration equal to that of the filter's impulse response. Similarly, if we were to switch the input off again suddenly, we would see a stop transient of the same duration. Such transients are an entirely necessary aspect of using LTI processors, and cannot be avoided. They occur in analog, as well as digital, processors.

So far we have treated digital convolution as a non-recursive operation, in which $x[n]$ and $h[n]$ are convolved to produce $y[n]$. Indeed a non-recursive difference equation such as equation (1.1) is equivalent to the convolution sum, equation (1.17). The coefficients by which input samples are multiplied are simply equal to successive terms in $h[n]$. However when we use a recursive difference equation such as equation (1.3) to compute an output signal, we are also in effect performing a convolution. It is implicit rather than explicit, and may be a little hard to visualise because the multiplier coefficients are not obviously related to the impulse response terms. Of course we can always generate $h[n]$ from such an equation term-by-term, and use it to implement a non-recursive version of the same processor. But in most cases we prefer to use the recursive form (if available), because it involves less computation.

1.4 Fourier Analysis

Our aim in the following sections is to show how Fourier Analysis can be applied to digital signals. In particular, we discuss two Fourier representations – a discrete-time version of the *Fourier Series*, which applies to strictly periodic digital signals; and a discrete-time version of the *Fourier Transform*, relevant to aperiodic signals and LTI processors. You will see that there are many similarities with classical continuous-time Fourier Analysis, as well as a few important differences.

We should mention at this point that there is a third type of Fourier representation, known as the *Discrete Fourier Transform (DFT)*, which is of key significance for the computer analysis of digital signals and systems. The DFT is widely implemented using so-called *Fast Fourier Transform (FFT)* algorithms. Not surprisingly, these techniques are closely related to the work of this chapter. However they are of such central importance to DSP that we give them special treatment in chapter 3.

One further point should be made. At this stage of our discussion we will generally assume that signals are real time functions, because they are easier to visualise. However we shall discuss complex signals in chapter 3, during our work on the DFT.

1.4.1 The Discrete Fourier Series

A periodic digital signal can be represented by a Fourier Series. Like its analog counterpart, it has a line spectrum. The features of such a line spectrum form a good starting point for our discussion of digital Fourier Analysis. Rather than get too involved in mathematical derivations and details, let us start with a definition, and illustrate it with the aid of a computer program.

Suppose we have a periodic digital signal which repeats every N sample values. The coefficients of its line spectrum indicate the 'amount' of various frequencies present in the signal. They may be found using the equation

$$a_k = \frac{1}{N} \sum_{k=0}^{N-1} x[n] \exp(-j2\pi kn/N)$$

where a_k represents the kth spectral component, or harmonic. This is known as the *analysis equation* of the Discrete Fourier Series. Conversely, if we know the coefficients a_k, we may regenerate $x(n)$ using the *synthesis* equation:

$$x[n] = \sum_{k=0}^{N-1} a_k \exp(j2\pi kn/N)$$

(Note that, in some texts, the $1/N$ multiplier appears in the synthesis equation rather than in the analysis equation. However, this is not an important difference, since it is only a scaling factor. An advantage of the present definition is that it leads naturally to the Fourier Transform equations derived in the next section.)

We see that the analysis and synthesis equations are very similar in form. The process of transforming from the time domain to the frequency domain is essentially the same as that of inverse transformation – going from the frequency domain back to the time domain.

Note that equation (1.21) specifies N separate harmonics for a signal with N samples per period. In other words there is an equal number of degrees of freedom in the time and frequency domains – an intuitively appealing result. Half this number of harmonics is adequate if $x[n]$ is real, since it turns out that the other half are simply their complex conjugates. And if we were to use the equation to compute further harmonics outside the range $n = 0$ to $(N - 1)$, we would find that they formed a repetitive sequence. Thus periodic digital signals (unlike their analog counterparts) have line spectra which repeat indefinitely along the frequency axis. This is just another aspect of the repetitive nature of sampled signal spectra, already discussed in section 1.2. It need cause no confusion. As long as we have obeyed the Sampling Theorem and avoided aliasing, it is only the first repetition which reflects frequencies present in the underlying analog signal. The rest are simply a consequence of sampling.

The harmonics a_k in equation (1.21) are generally complex, and are conveniently expressed in terms of magnitude and phase. Computer Program 2 in appendix A calculates them for any signal with 64 samples per period ($N = 64$), and produces a screen plot. In figure 1.16 we have used the program to illustrate the magnitude and phase spectrum of a signal with just a few sine and cosine components, given by

$$x[n] = \sin(2\pi n/64) + \cos(2\pi n/16) + 0.6\cos(2\pi n/8)$$

$$+ 0.5\sin(2\pi n/4), \quad 0 \leqslant n \leqslant 63 \tag{1.23}$$

Its four components have 64, 16, 8 and 4 samples per period respectively, corresponding to the fundamental, 4th harmonic, 8th harmonic and 16th harmonic. The composite signal repeats every 64 sampling intervals.

The magnitudes of spectral coefficients a_0 to a_{63} inclusive are plotted in part (b) of the figure. As expected, only a_1, a_4, a_8 and a_{16} – and their complex conjugate 'mirror images' – are non-zero. The mirror image pattern, which arises because $x[n]$ is real, means that half the coefficients (a_0 to a_{32}) are sufficient to define the spectrum completely in this case.

The phases plotted in part (c) of the figure show which of the components are sines, and which cosines. For example, a_1 and a_{63} have phases of $\pm\pi/2$, representing a sine; whereas a_4 and a_{60} both have zero phase, and denote a cosine. Of course, in the more general case there would be a mixture of sine and cosine components at each harmonic

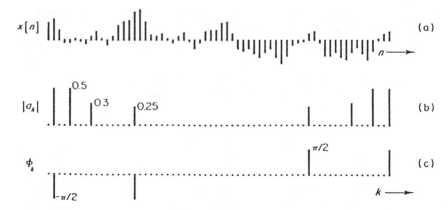

Figure 1.16 Computed spectral coefficients of a periodic signal with several sine and cosine components (*abscissa: 64 samples*)

frequency, giving phases with intermediate values between 0 and $\pm\pi/2$.

Such phase spectra may be a little hard to interpret, because a computer arctan function returns a value between $\pm\pi/2$ (remember that $\tan(a) = \tan(a + \pi)$). Furthermore, care must be taken when estimating the phase if the real or imaginary part of a harmonic is very small, or zero. Otherwise spurious phase values may be obtained. Computer Program 2 includes a number of additional statements to prevent this happening.

The four frequency components of the signal in figure 1.16 each complete an integral number of cycles, or periods, between $n = 0$ and $n = 64$. Since $x[n]$ is assumed to be repeated end-on-end, the natural periodicity of each component is preserved, and there are no sudden discontinuities. The resulting spectrum is well-behaved, each component occupying a definite harmonic frequency.

The situation is however rather different if $x[n]$ contains sinusoids which do not display an exact number of periods between $n = 0$ and $n = 64$. Computer Program 2 may easily be adapted to demonstrate the effect. For example, figure 1.17 shows a cosine with two and a half periods. Repeated end-on-end, this signal displays sudden discontinuities. Furthermore, unlike an eternal cosine, it is not an even function of n. So its spectrum is likely to display complicated phase relationships.

Since the cosine goes through two and a half periods within each period of $x[n]$, we may expect its spectral energy to be concentrated close to $k = 2$ and $k = 3$. This is confirmed by part (b) of the figure. However the spectrum is complicated, with a lot of spreading, or *leakage*, of energy due to the discontinuities; and the phase relationships between the various components are hard to visualise. It is a good example of the effects which discontinuities can have on the spectrum of an otherwise 'straightforward' signal.

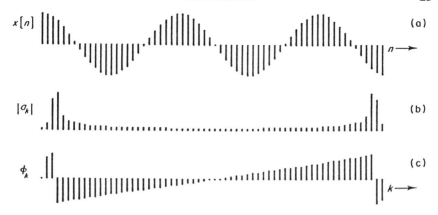

Figure 1.17 The spectrum of a periodic signal with sudden discontinuities (*abscissa: 64 samples*)

It is also instructive to investigate the spectrum of an impulse. Figure 1.18 shows the screen plot obtained when a unit impulse $\delta[n]$ forms the input signal to Computer Program 2. We must of course remember that all signals in this section are considered periodic, and our program assumes 64 samples per period. We are therefore finding the spectrum of an impulse train, not an individual impulse. Nevertheless, the results give us some valuable insights.

We see that all the spectral coefficients are equal in this case. The signal's energy is evenly distributed in the frequency domain. This suggests why 'impulse testing' of an LTI processor is so effective: it simultaneously delivers an equal amount of all frequencies to the processor's input. The impulse response of the processor therefore characterises its performance completely.

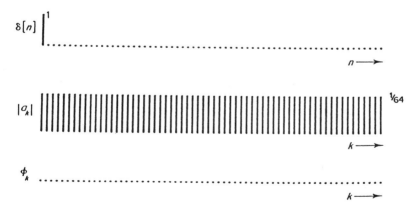

Figure 1.18 Computed spectrum of an impulse train (*abscissa: 64 samples*)

Before ending this brief account of the Discrete Fourier Series, we should summarise some of its most important properties. These can often help us estimate a signal's spectrum, and they shed additional light on the relationships between time and frequency domains. The most important properties are: *linearity*; *time-shifting*; *differentiation*; *integration*; *convolution*; and *modulation*.

In the following discussion we use a double-headed arrow to denote the relationship between a signal and its spectrum. Thus $x[n] \leftrightarrow a_k$ signifies that the periodic digital signal $x[n]$ has spectral coefficients a_k. $x[n]$ transforms into a_k; a_k inverse transforms into $x[n]$. We should regard the time-domain and frequency-domain descriptions of a signal as entirely equivalent. Which we choose to work with on a particular occasion is essentially a matter of convenience.

The *linearity* property is straightforward, and may be stated as follows:

If

$$x_1[n] \leftrightarrow a_k \quad \text{and} \quad x_2[n] \leftrightarrow b_k$$

Then

$$Ax_1[n] + Bx_2[n] \leftrightarrow Aa_k + Bb_k \tag{1.24}$$

where A and B are constants. Thus the spectra of two (or more) weighted, superposed, signals equals the weighted sum of their individual spectra. Remember, however, that the summation of spectra must take account of phase as well as magnitude.

The *time-shifting* property is as follows:

If

$$x[n] \leftrightarrow a_k$$

Then

$$x[n - n_0] \leftrightarrow a_k \exp(-j2\pi k n_0/N) \tag{1.25}$$

This defines the effect on the spectrum of shifting $x[n]$ by n_0 sampling intervals. The exponential changes the phases of the coefficients, but not their magnitudes. Note that if we put $n_0 = N$, the signal is shifted by one complete period, and

$$\exp(-j2\pi k n_0/N) = \exp(-j2\pi k) = 1$$

for all values of k. Therefore, as expected, the spectrum is unaltered.

When discussing time shifts in relation to the Discrete Fourier Series, we should be clear that all the shifts involved are *periodic*, or *circular*. That is to say, a shift by n_0 is indistinguishable from a shift by $(n_0 + mN)$, where N

is the period and m is an integer. An alternative way of looking at this is to say that all shifts should be evaluated *modulo-N*.

The *differentiation* property may be expressed as follows:

If

$$x[n] \leftrightarrow a_k$$

Then

$$x[n] - x[n-1] \leftrightarrow a_k \{1 - \exp(-j2\pi k/N)\} \tag{1.26}$$

Note that we are interpreting 'differentiation' as forming the first-order difference of $x[n]$. This gives a simple estimate of the slope of the signal. The above result then follows directly from the linearity and time-shifting properties.

Provided the dc component a_0 of a periodic digital signal is zero, the following *integration* property holds good:

If

$$x[n] \leftrightarrow a_k$$

Then

$$\sum_{k=-\infty}^{n} x[k] \leftrightarrow a_k \{1 - \exp(-j2\pi k/N)\}^{-1} \tag{1.27}$$

We are defining 'integration' as forming the running sum of $x[n]$. This property is essentially the opposite, or *inverse*, of the differentiation property defined by expression (1.26).

Let us next consider the *convolution* property. If the digital signals $x_1[n]$ and $x_2[n]$ have the same period, and

If

$$x_1[n] \leftrightarrow a_k \quad \text{and} \quad x_2[n] \leftrightarrow b_k$$

Then

$$\sum_{m=0}^{N-1} x_1[m]x_2[n-m] \leftrightarrow Na_kb_k \tag{1.28}$$

The left-hand side of the expression denotes a convolution over one period. This ensures convergence of the summation. The operation is called *circular*, or *periodic*, convolution, and is often given the symbol ⊛. We may visualise circular convolution as the placing of the N samples of $x_1[n]$ around the circumference of a cylinder, and the N samples of $x_2[n]$ in reverse order around another, concentric cylinder. One cylinder is rotated, and coincident samples of $x_1[n]$ and $x_2[n]$ are multiplied and summed. Expression (1.28) shows that such time-domain convolution is equivalent to frequency-domain multiplication.

The time- and frequency-domain descriptions of a signal are essentially equivalent. They are like the two sides of a coin. Therefore it should cause no surprise that time-domain multiplication is equivalent to frequency-domain convolution. This is summarised by the *modulation* property of the Discrete Fourier Series. It may be stated as follows:

If

$$x_1[n] \leftrightarrow a_k \quad \text{and} \quad x_2[n] \leftrightarrow b_k$$

Then

$$x_1[n]\, x_2[n] \leftrightarrow \sum_{m=0}^{N-1} a_m b_{k-m} \tag{1.29}$$

For convenience, we summarize the main properties of the Discrete Fourier Series as table B.1 in appendix B.

1.4.2 The Fourier Transform

Most practical digital signals are *aperiodic* – that is, they are not strictly repetitive. Good examples are the share price illustrated in figure 1.1 and the EMG signal in figure 1.3. It is worth noting that from a communications engineering point of view, a certain amount of randomness is essential if a signal is to convey useful information. It is therefore important to appreciate how Fourier Analysis applies to aperiodic sequences. The relevant technique is the *Fourier Transform*.

We should straight away add that the Discrete Fourier Series described in the previous section is by no means redundant. It is very closely related to the transform, and to computer analysis using the DFT. We shall explore this important matter in chapter 3.

A common way of developing the Fourier Transform for digital signals is via the continuous-time Fourier Transform, as used in analog signal and system analysis. However, since this book is concerned with DSP, we prefer a digital approach. We will start with the Discrete Fourier Series equations, and modify them to cope with aperiodic signals.

The analysis equation of the Discrete Fourier Series, already defined by equation (1.21), is

$$a_k = \frac{1}{N} \sum_{n=0}^{N-1} x[n] \exp(-j2\pi kn/N) \qquad (1.30)$$

It applies, of course, to a strictly periodic signal of period N. Each spectral coefficient, or harmonic, is found by multiplying $x[n]$ by an exponential of the appropriate frequency, and summing over one period. Note that, although the equation specifies the period between $n = 0$ and $(N - 1)$, any other complete period will do equally well.

Now suppose we 'stretch' adjacent repetitions of the signal apart, filling the gaps between them with zeros. This is illustrated by figure 1.19. Part (a) shows an arbitrary periodic signal with 5 samples per period ($N = 5$). In part (b) we have separated adjacent repetitions, creating a signal for which $N = 12$. By continuing this process we could, in principle, make $N \to \infty$. The signal would have just 5 finite sample values centred at $n = 0$, the neighbouring repetitions having moved away towards $\pm\infty$. We would be left with an aperiodic signal.

What happens to the spectral coefficients a_k if we stretch the signal in this way? First, we note that they must become smaller, because of the $(1/N)$ multiplier in equation (1.30). Secondly, it is clear they must come closer together in frequency, because N also appears in the denominator of the exponential. In the limit as $N \to \infty$, the various harmonics bunch together extremely closely and have vanishingly small amplitudes. We

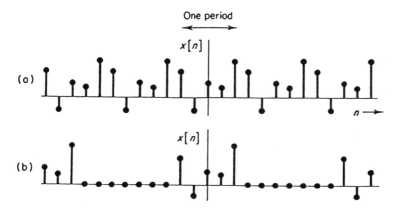

Figure 1.19 'Stretching' a periodic signal

must now think in terms of a continuous, rather than discrete, distribution of spectral energy.

Although each spectral coefficient becomes vanishingly small as $N \rightarrow \infty$, the product Na_k remains finite. Let us write it as X. We will also write $(2\pi k/N)$ as Ω, and think of it as a continuous frequency variable. Equation (1.30) becomes

$$X = Na_k = \sum_{n=0}^{N-1} x[n] \exp(-j\Omega n) \tag{1.31}$$

The limits of summation should also be changed, to take account of the fact that $x[n]$ is now aperiodic. In general, $x[n]$ will exist for both positive and negative values of n, so we will sum between $n = \pm\infty$. A further minor change is to write X as $X(\Omega)$, making clear that it is a function of the frequency Ω. Thus

$$X(\Omega) = \sum_{n=-\infty}^{\infty} x[n] \exp(-j\Omega n) \tag{1.32}$$

This important equation defines the Fourier Transform $X(\Omega)$ of an aperiodic signal $x[n]$.

Using similar arguments and substitutions, we can develop the *inverse transform* from the synthesis equation of the Discrete Fourier Series. The inverse transform tells us how to derive the signal $x[n]$ from its spectrum $X(\Omega)$. The synthesis equation, equation (1.22), is

$$x[n] = \sum_{k=0}^{N-1} a_k \exp(j2\pi kn/N) \tag{1.33}$$

In this case it is helpful to substitute Ω_0 for $2\pi/N$, which equals the first harmonic, or *fundamental*, frequency. Thus $\Omega = k\Omega_0$, and

$$x[n] = \sum_{k=0}^{N-1} \left\{ \frac{X(k\Omega_0)}{N} \right\} \exp(jk\Omega_0 n) \tag{1.34}$$

Furthermore, since $1/N = \Omega_0/2\pi$ we have

$$x[n] = \frac{1}{2\pi} \sum_{k=0}^{N-1} X(k\Omega_0) \exp(jk\Omega_0 n)\, \Omega_0 \tag{1.35}$$

Now as $N \to \infty$ and $\Omega_0 \to 0$, the summation becomes an integration. Since the spectrum of a digital signal is always periodic, we integrate over one spectral period – equivalent to an interval of 2π in Ω. Furthermore, we write Ω_0, which becomes vanishingly small, as $d\Omega$. We finally obtain:

$$x[n] = \frac{1}{2\pi} \int_{2\pi} X(\Omega) \exp(j\Omega n) \, d\Omega \qquad (1.36)$$

Equations (1.32) and (1.36) are key results, and constitute a discrete-time *Fourier Transform pair*. There are many similarities with the classic Fourier Transform pair applied to analog signals. However there is one major difference: the spectrum of a digital signal is always repetitive.

You may find the Fourier Transform a little hard to visualise, so we will illustrate with two examples.

Suppose we wish to find the frequency spectrum of the aperiodic signal shown in part (a) of figure 1.20. Equation (1.32) gives

$$x[\Omega] = \sum_{n=-\infty}^{\infty} x[n] \exp(-j\Omega n)$$

$$= 0.5 + 0.25 \exp(-j\Omega) + 0.125 \exp(-j2\Omega) + \dots$$

$$= 0.5 \sum_{n=0}^{\infty} \{0.5 \exp(-j\Omega)\}^n$$

$$= 0.5/\{1 - 0.5 \exp(-j\Omega)\} \qquad (1.37)$$

We are often mainly interested in the spectral magnitude, which is given by

$$|X(\Omega)| = \frac{0.5}{\{(1 - 0.5 \cos\Omega)^2 + (0.5 \sin\Omega)^2\}^{1/2}}$$

$$= \frac{0.5}{(1 - \cos\Omega + 0.25 \cos^2\Omega + 0.25 \sin^2\Omega)^{1/2}}$$

$$= \frac{0.5}{(1.25 - \cos\Omega)^{1/2}} \qquad (1.38)$$

The function is sketched in part (b) of the figure. Note the repetitive nature of the spectrum, and the continuous distribution of spectral energy. The range $\Omega = 0$ to 2π corresponds to the frequency axis in figures 1.16–1.18;

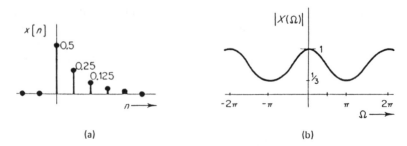

Figure 1.20   An aperiodic signal and its spectrum

and half this range ($\Omega = 0$ to π) is sufficient to define the spectrum of any adequately sampled real signal. Within this range, we see that our signal is richest in low frequencies around $\Omega = 0$.

In the previous section we used a computer program to estimate the Discrete Fourier Series of an impulse train (figure 1.18), and showed that it contained an equal amount of all harmonic frequencies. For the sake of completeness – and also because impulse functions are of such importance in DSP – let us now find the Fourier Transform of an isolated unit impulse. We have

$$X(\Omega) = \sum_{n=-\infty}^{\infty} x[n] \exp(-j\Omega n) = \sum_{n=-\infty}^{\infty} \delta[n] \exp(-j\Omega n) \qquad (1.39)$$

Since the unit impulse has the value 1 at $n = 0$ and is zero elsewhere, the above summation has just one non-zero term, which must equal the value of $\exp(-j\Omega n)$ at $n = 0$ (this reflects the so-called *sifting* property of the unit impulse). Hence

$$X(\Omega) = \exp(-j\Omega n)\big|_{n=0} = 1 \qquad (1.40)$$

We see that $\delta[n]$ contains an equal amount of all frequencies; and $X(\Omega)$, which is best thought of as a frequency density function, is a constant. This result implies that $\delta[n]$ could be synthesised from an infinite set of cosines, all of vanishingly small, but equal, amplitudes. The signal and its spectrum are shown in figure 1.21. Since the spectrum is real in this case, it can be fully represented by a single diagram.

The foregoing examples show that it is quite easy to find Fourier Transforms – at least for simple signals. We could certainly extend our 'library' of results to other types of signal. However, the normal approach is to use a look-up table, as supplied in many books and references on

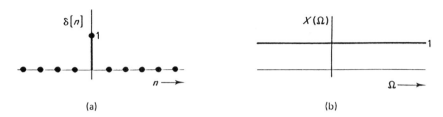

Figure 1.21　An isolated unit impulse and its spectrum

Fourier Analysis. We include a few important transforms and inverse transforms as part of table B.2 in appendix B.

We described some important properties of the Discrete Fourier Series at the end of the previous section, and these are summarised in table B.1 of appendix B. Not surprisingly, the Fourier Transform possesses an equivalent set of properties, summarised in table B.2. If you compare the two tables, you will see many parallels. From the point of view of our work in this book, the most important properties of the Fourier Transform are *linearity*, *time-shifting*, and *convolution*. In particular, table B.2 shows that a time-shift is equivalent to multiplying by an imaginary exponential in the frequency domain; and that time-domain convolution is equivalent to frequency-domain multiplication.

So far we have used the Fourier Transform to investigate the spectra of aperiodic digital signals. We now turn to another extremely useful application – its ability to describe the frequency-domain performance of LTI processors.

The key relationships defining an LTI processor in the time and frequency domains are illustrated in figure 1.22. In the time domain, the input signal $x[n]$ is convolved with the impulse response $h[n]$ to produce the output signal $y[n]$. The convolution property of the Fourier Transform tells us that the equivalent frequency domain operation must be a

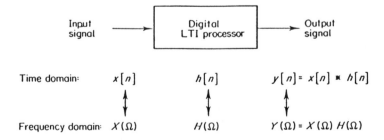

Figure 1.22　Time- and frequency-domain descriptions of signal flow through an LTI processor

multiplication. The output signal spectrum $Y[\Omega]$ is the product of the input signal spectrum $X(\Omega)$ and the frequency response of the processor $H(\Omega)$. When forming this product we must, of course, take proper account of phase as well as magnitude.

The impulse response $h[n]$ and the frequency response $H(\Omega)$ are a Fourier Transform pair. The relationship is quite easy to demonstrate. If we deliver a unit impulse to the processor input, then $x[n] = \delta[n]$. But we have already seen that the spectrum of a unit impulse is unity (equation (1.40)), so in this case $X(\Omega) = 1$. Therefore

$$Y(\Omega) = X(\Omega)\,H(\Omega) = H(\Omega) \tag{1.41}$$

Since $y[n]$ clearly equals $h[n]$, it follows that $h[n]$ must transform into $H(\Omega)$.

We are now in a position to define the frequency response of practical processors, and will illustrate with two examples. Consider first the decaying exponential already illustrated in part (a) of figure 1.20. Although we have so far treated it as a signal $x[n]$, it could just as easily represent the impulse response $h[n]$ of a causal, stable, LTI processor. In that case the Fourier Transform we calculated in equation (1.37) would represent the equivalent frequency response $H(\Omega)$. Its magnitude, shown in part (b) of the figure, represents a simple low-pass filter, since over the range $\Omega = 0$ to π (which is the range occupied by any adequately-sampled input signal) the response peaks around $\Omega = 0$. Note that in this example we have derived the frequency response by direct transformation of the impulse response.

An alternative is to work from a processor's difference equation. Indeed this is the sensible approach in the case of a recursive processor, since we do not normally wish to go to the trouble of finding, and then transforming, its impulse response. In general the difference equation of an LTI processor takes the form:

$$\sum_{k=0}^{N} a_k\, y[n-k] = \sum_{k=0}^{M} b_k\, x[n-k] \tag{1.42}$$

where terms a_k represent recursive, and b_k non-recursive, multiplier coefficients. (*Note:* we have previously used the symbol a_k in this chapter to denote the spectral coefficients of a Discrete Fourier Series. Furthermore, we are now using N to denote the order of the processor – not the period of a periodic signal. Such are the difficulties of finding enough symbols for a book on DSP!)

We may write the Fourier Transform of both sides of equation (1.42) as follows:

$$\sum_{k=0}^{N} a_k \exp(-jk\Omega) \, Y(\Omega) = \sum_{k=0}^{M} b_k \exp(-jk\Omega) \, X(\Omega) \tag{1.43}$$

This result stems directly from the linearity and time-shifting properties of the transform. Now $Y(\Omega) = X(\Omega) \, H(\Omega)$, so that

$$H(\Omega) = \frac{Y(\Omega)}{X(\Omega)} = \frac{\displaystyle\sum_{k=0}^{M} b_k \exp(-jk\Omega)}{\displaystyle\sum_{k=0}^{N} a_k \exp(-jk\Omega)} \tag{1.44}$$

The equation is quite general, and allows us to compute $H(\Omega)$ for any LTI processor.

Take, for example, the notch filter used to suppress supply-frequency interference from an EMG (see figure 1.3). Its difference equation is

$$y[n] = 1.9556y[n-1] - 0.9801y[n-2] + x[n] - 1.9754x[n-1] + x[n-2] \tag{1.45}$$

Using equation (1.44) we obtain

$$H(\Omega) = \left\{ \frac{1 - 1.9754 \exp(-j\Omega) + \exp(-2j\Omega)}{1 - 1.9556 \exp(-j\Omega) + 0.9801 \exp(-2j\Omega)} \right\} \tag{1.46}$$

Figure 1.23 shows the computed magnitude of this function. Over most of the range $\Omega = 0$ to π, the filter transmits input frequency components with unity gain. But there is a deep notch at $\Omega = 0.05\pi$ which must, of course, coincide with the supply frequency. Now $\Omega = 0.05\pi$ corresponds to a sinusoid with 40 samples per period. Therefore if the supply frequency is 50 Hz, we must use a sampling frequency of 2 kHz; if the supply frequency is 60 Hz, we must sample at 2.4 kHz – as already noted in section 1.1.

Although we are now able to analyse the frequency-domain performance of an LTI processor, we are not quite ready to tackle the problem of *synthesis*, or design. We will get closer to this in the next section on the z-Transform, and begin the task in earnest in chapter 2.

Figure 1.23 Magnitude response of a notch filter (*abscissa: 320 samples*)

1.5 The z-Transform

The z-Transform offers a valuable set of techniques for the frequency-domain analysis of digital signals and processors, and is very useful in design. It should be regarded as complementary to, rather than distinct from, the Fourier Transform. However whereas Fourier techniques originated in the analog domain, the z-Transform is inherently concerned with sampled signals and systems. It provides an extremely compact and convenient notation, which is widely used by DSP designers; and offers a *pole–zero* description of LTI processors which is a great help in visualising their frequency response and stability characteristics.

We shall restrict ourselves here to some of the most basic and important aspects of the transform – and particularly those needed for the design of recursive digital filters in chapter 2. Much fuller treatments of the z-Transform are given in several of the books listed in the Bibliography at the end of this book.

1.5.1 Definition and properties

The z-Transform of a digital signal is defined as:

$$X(z) = \sum_{n=0}^{\infty} x[n]\, z^{-n} \tag{1.47}$$

Note that we are using the *unilateral* version of the transform, with summation limits of $n = 0$ to ∞. This version is adequate for digital signals which may be considered zero prior to $n = 0$, and for causal processors. An alternative, *bilateral*, version is sometimes used; however it has much more stringent convergence conditions, and will not be considered here.

Equation (1.47) is quite easy to visualise. $X(z)$ is essentially a *power series in* z^{-1}, with coefficients equal to successive values of the time-domain signal. Therefore if we express any z-Transform as a power series, we can immediately regenerate the signal. This may not be the most economical way of proceeding – but it is always possible in principle.

Let us take two simple examples. First, we find the z-Transform of the exponentially decaying signal in part (a) of figure 1.24. Using equation (1.47) we have:

$$X(z) = \sum_{n=0}^{\infty} x[n]\, z^{-n}$$

$$= 1 + 0.8z^{-1} + 0.64z^{-2} + 0.512z^{-3} + \dots$$

$$= 1/(1 - 0.8z^{-1}) = z/(z - 0.8) \tag{1.48}$$

Note the compact form of this result. We have described a signal with an infinite number of sample values by a very simple expression in z.

For our second example, let us work the other way round: given a z-Transform, we will find the corresponding signal. Suppose the transform is

$$X(z) = 1/(z + 1.2) \tag{1.49}$$

We may express this as a power series in z^{-1} as follows:

$$X(z) = \frac{1}{(z + 1.2)} = \frac{z^{-1}}{(1 + 1.2z^{-1})} = z^{-1}\,(1 + 1.2z^{-1})^{-1}$$

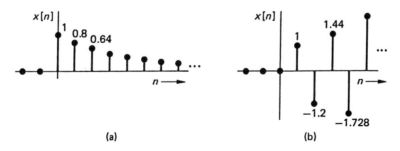

(a)   (b)

Figure 1.24

$$= z^{-1} \{1 + (-1.2z^{-1}) + (-1.2z^{-1})^2 + \ldots\}$$

$$= z^{-1} - 1.2z^{-2} + 1.44z^{-3} - 1.728z^{-4} + \ldots \tag{1.50}$$

Successive values of $x[n]$, starting at $n = 0$, are therefore

$$0, 1, -1.2, 1.44, -1.728, \ldots$$

The signal is shown in part (b) of the figure. Note that this particular function grows without limit as $n \to \infty$, and could not therefore represent either a real-life signal, or the impulse response of a stable processor.

If we substitute $\exp(j\Omega)$ for z in equation (1.47), we obtain:

$$X(\Omega) = \sum_{n=0}^{\infty} x[n] \exp(-j\Omega n) \tag{1.51}$$

Apart from a change in the lower limit of summation, this is identical to the Fourier Transform given by equation (1.32). It is therefore clear that the z-Transform and the Fourier Transform are closely related. We shall return to this important point in the next section.

An alternative, and probably simpler, way of thinking of z is as a *time-shift operator*. Multiplication by z is equivalent to a time *advance* by one sampling interval. Division by z is equivalent to a time *delay* by the same amount. For example, a unit impulse at $n = 0$ has the z-Transform:

$$X(z) = \sum_{n=0}^{\infty} \delta[n] z^{-n} = z^{-n} \bigg|_{n=0} = 1 \tag{1.52}$$

A unit impulse delayed by n_0 sampling intervals has the transform:

$$X(z) = \sum_{n=0}^{\infty} \delta[n - n_0] z^{-n} = z^{-n} \bigg|_{n=n_0} = z^{-n_0} \tag{1.53}$$

Notice how the transform converts a time-shift into a simple algebraic manipulation in the frequency domain.

In view of its simplicity, it may seem a little surprising that the z-Transform gives us all the advantages of a frequency-domain approach to signal and system analysis. As far as DSP is concerned, one of the most important advantages stems from its *convolution property*, which states that time-domain convolution is equivalent to frequency-domain multiplication. This property is, of course, shared by the Fourier Transform – as we showed in the previous section. It means that the output from an LTI processor can either be found by convolving its input signal and impulse response, or by multiplying their z-Transforms. The latter is normally a very straightforward operation.

So far we have recovered a signal from its z-Transform by expanding the latter as a power series. We should now consider the process of inverse transformation more carefully. Formally, the inverse transform of a function $X(z)$ is defined as

$$x[n] = \frac{1}{2\pi j} \oint X(z) \, z^{n-1} \, dz \qquad (1.54)$$

where the circular symbol on the integral sign denotes a closed contour in the complex plane. Such contour integration is beyond the scope of this section. Fortunately, however, several alternative approaches are available. As already noted, one is to express $X(z)$ as a power series. Another is to look up the function we need in a table of z-Transform pairs. Such tables are common in the DSP literature, and we include a short one as table B.3 in appendix B. If the function is not listed, it may be possible to express it as the sum of two or more simpler functions which do appear in the table, using the algebraic method of partial fractions.

Yet another approach, which is often highly convenient, is to derive $x[n]$ from $X(z)$ using a recursive computer algorithm. A good way of explaining the method is to assume that the z-Transform in question represents the transfer function $H(z)$ of an LTI processor, rather than a signal. In this case the corresponding time function must correspond to the processor's impulse response $h[n]$. Now, in general

$$Y(z) = X(z) \, H(z) \quad \text{or} \quad H(z) = \frac{Y(z)}{X(z)} \qquad (1.55)$$

where $Y(z)$ and $X(z)$ are the z-Transforms of the output and input signals respectively. These frequency-domain relationships are precisely equivalent to those for the Fourier Transform described previously.

The method is as follows: we first derive the difference equation corresponding to $H(z)$; we then deliver a unit impulse as the input signal, and compute the impulse response $h[n]$. This must equal the inverse z-Transform we are seeking.

As an example, consider the complicated z-Transform:

$$\frac{z^2(z - 1)(z^2 + 1)}{(z + 0.8)(z^2 + 1.38593z + 0.9604)(z^2 - 1.64545z + 0.9025)} \qquad (1.56)$$

We multiply out the numerator and denominator, and assume the function represents an LTI processor. Thus

$$H(z) = \frac{Y(z)}{X(z)}$$

$$= \frac{z^5 - z^4 + z^3 - z^2}{(z^5 + 0.54048z^4 - 0.62519z^3 - 0.66354z^2 + 0.60317z + 0.69341)}$$

(1.57)

The corresponding difference equation is readily obtained:

$$y[n] = -0.54048y[n - 1] + 0.62519y[n - 2] + 0.66354y[n - 3]$$

$$-0.60317y[n - 4] - 0.69341y[n - 5] + x[n]$$

$$- x[n - 1] + x[n - 2] - x[n - 3]$$

(1.58)

If we now replace $x[n]$ by the unit impulse function $\delta[n]$, $y[n]$ must become $h[n]$ – and we have a recursive algorithm for computing the required inverse transform. Figure 1.25 shows the result of this computation. It reveals a complicated decaying signal with a number of frequency components – a function which would certainly be tedious to find by other methods. Note however that we end up with a sequence of sample values, rather than an analytical expression. Whether or not this is a disadvantage depends upon the application.

The z-Transform, like the Fourier Transform, has a number of useful properties. We have previously mentioned the convolution property, and have described the role of z as a time-shift operator. The other major

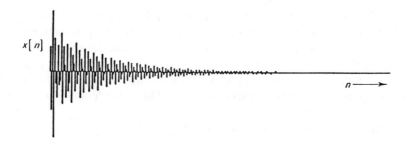

Figure 1.25   An inverse z-Transform evaluated by computer (*abscissa: 320 samples*)

properties of interest in DSP are listed in table B.4 in appendix B. If you compare them with the corresponding properties of the Fourier Transform (see table B.2), you will notice obvious similarities. In particular, z is equivalent to $\exp(j\Omega)$.

We have now covered the basic notation and properties of the z-Transform. The next task is to introduce z-plane poles and zeros, and outline their importance in analysis and design.

1.5.2   z-Plane poles and zeros

A z-Transform which describes a real digital signal or an LTI processor is always a rational function of z. In other words it can be written as the ratio of numerator and denominator polynomials:

$$X(z) = \frac{N(z)}{D(z)} \tag{1.59}$$

This is true whether $X(z)$ represents an input or output signal, or the transfer function of a processor. Apart from a gain factor K it follows that the transform may be completely specified by the roots of $N(z)$ and $D(z)$. In general we may write:

$$X(z) = \frac{N(z)}{D(z)} = K \frac{(z - z_1)(z - z_2)(z - z_3) \ldots}{(z - p_1)(z - p_2)(z - p_3) \ldots} \tag{1.60}$$

The constants $z_1, z_2, z_3 \ldots$ are called the *zeros* of $X(z)$; the constants p_1, $p_2, p_3 \ldots$ are called the *poles*. It is found that whenever the corresponding time function is real, then the poles and zeros are themselves either real, or occur in complex conjugate pairs. In all these respects z-plane poles and zeros are similar to their s-plane counterparts in continuous-time analysis.

A very useful representation of a z-Transform is obtained by plotting its poles and zeros in the complex z-plane. This is done in table B.3 in appendix B for a number of useful transform pairs. For example, we see from the table that a sinusoidal signal, switched on at $n = 0$, has a zero at the origin and a complex conjugate pole pair on a circle of unit radius, referred to as the *unit circle*.

If a z-Transform represents the transfer function of a system, its pole positions give important information about system stability. For example, suppose we have a processor with a single real pole at $z = \alpha$. Then

$$H(z) = \frac{Y(z)}{X(z)} = \frac{1}{(z - \alpha)} \tag{1.61}$$

or

$$z\,Y(z) - \alpha Y(z) = X(z) \tag{1.62}$$

The processor's difference equation is

$$y[n + 1] - \alpha y[n] = x[n]$$

or

$$y[n] = \alpha y[n - 1] + x[n - 1] \tag{1.63}$$

By delivering a unit impulse $\delta[n]$ at the input, it is simple to show that successive impulse response terms, starting at $n = 0$, are

$$0, 1, \alpha, \alpha^2, \alpha^3, \alpha^4 \ldots$$

It follows that if the magnitude of α is less than unity, the impulse response decays towards zero, and the processor is stable. But if the magnitude of α is greater than unity, the impulse response grows without limit, denoting an unstable system. Therefore, for stability, the pole must lie *inside the unit circle* in the z-plane.

Similar arguments can be applied to complex conjugate pole-pairs. For example, a processor defined by a pair of poles on the imaginary axis at $z = \pm j\alpha$ has an impulse response $h[n]$ with successive terms:

$$0, 0, 1, 0, -\alpha^2, 0, \alpha^4, 0, -\alpha^6, 0 \ldots$$

Once again this grows without limit if $|\alpha| > 1$. We conclude that, for a stable processor, the poles must be inside the unit circle. The same applies to complex poles lying away from the real and imaginary axes: if their radius (measured from the z-plane origin) is greater than unity, they produce an unstable system.

Since stability is intimately related to the radius of z-plane poles, it is often helpful to express their locations in polar coordinates. Suppose we have a processor with a complex conjugate pole-pair, as shown in part (a) of figure 1.26. The poles are at radius r, and make angle $\pm\theta$ with the positive real axis. The transfer function is therefore

$$H(z) = \frac{Y(z)}{X(z)} = \frac{1}{\{z - r\exp(j\theta)\}\{z - r\exp(-j\theta)\}}$$

$$= \frac{1}{(z^2 - 2rz\cos\theta + r^2)} \tag{1.64}$$

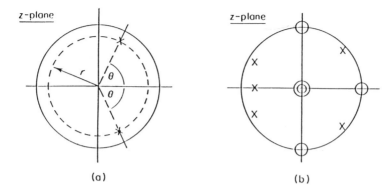

Figure 1.26   z-Plane poles and zeros

The corresponding difference equation is

$$y[n] = 2r \cos\theta\, y[n - 1] - r^2 y[n - 2] + x[n - 2] \qquad (1.65)$$

The processor will only be stable if $r < 1$, regardless of the value of θ.

We met a z-Transform with denominator factors similar to those of equation (1.64) at the end of the previous section. If you refer back to equation (1.56), you will see that the transform we considered had a real pole at $z = -0.8$, and two complex conjugate pole-pairs with denominator factors

$$(z^2 + 1.38593z + 0.9604) \quad \text{and} \quad (z^2 - 1.64545z + 0.9025)$$

Comparing with equation (1.64) we see that, for the first pole-pair:

$r^2 = 0.9064$ and $2r \cos\theta = -1.38593$

giving $r = 0.98$ and $\theta = 45°$ \qquad\qquad (1.66)

and for the second pole-pair:

$r^2 = 0.9025$ and $2r \cos\theta = 1.64545$

giving $r = 0.95$ and $\theta = 150°$ \qquad\qquad (1.67)

The complete pole–zero pattern for this transform is plotted in part (b) of figure 1.26. Since all poles lie inside the unit circle, we know that the corresponding time function must decay to zero as $n \to \infty$. This is confirmed by the computed result already shown in figure 1.25.

Note that our comments about stability and the unit circle apply only to poles. There are no corresponding restrictions on the location of zeros.

A further point concerns zeros (or poles) at the origin of the z-plane. These produce a pure time advance (or delay), but have no other effect on the characteristics of the processor or signal. For example, the processor defined by equations (1.64) and (1.65) has two z-plane poles, but no zeros. We see from its difference equation that each output value $y[n]$ depends on the input value $x[n - 2]$, implying a time delay of two sampling intervals. The impulse response begins at $n = 2$, not $n = 0$. Such a delay is unnecessary, and is normally considered undesirable. It is easily corrected by placing a second-order zero at the origin, equivalent to a numerator term z^2 in $H(z)$. In general, we achieve a minimum-delay processor by ensuring that there is an equal number of poles and zeros. Of course, if a function has more zeros than poles, we must add *poles* at the origin. Otherwise the impulse response will begin *before* $n = 0$, denoting a non-causal system.

We next turn our attention to the relationship between the z-Transform and the Fourier Transform, and show how the spectral function of a signal or processor can be visualised from a knowledge of its z-plane poles and zeros. The technique is often referred to as the *geometrical evaluation of the Fourier Transform in the z-plane*.

We have previously noted that the complex variable z is equivalent to $\exp(j\Omega)$ in Fourier notation. Therefore if we make this substitution, we are effectively converting from a z-Transform to the exponentials (or sines and cosines) of Fourier Analysis. To understand the relationship more fully, we should consider where values of $z = \exp(j\Omega)$ lie in the z-plane. Since $\exp(j\Omega)$ has unit magnitude for any real value of Ω, they must all lie *on the unit circle*. If $\Omega = 0, 2\pi, 4\pi, \ldots$ we are at the point $z = (1, j0)$ on the real axis; if $\Omega = \pi, 3\pi, 5\pi, \ldots$, we are at $(-1, j0)$. And as Ω increases, we move anticlockwise around the unit circle. This is shown by figure 1.27.

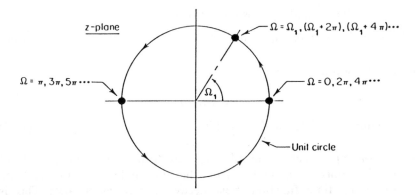

Figure 1.27   Sinusoidal frequencies corresponding to various points on the unit circle

We now see why the z-Transform gives such a compact description of digital signals and processors. We know from our work on Fourier Analysis that their spectral characteristics always repeat indefinitely along the frequency axis at intervals of 2π. The z-Transform takes the effect into account automatically, since any 2π interval is equivalent to one complete revolution around the unit circle in the z-plane.

We can use this new perspective to infer the frequency response of an LTI processor. Let us take a simple example – a processor with a pole at $z = -0.8$ and a zero at $z = 0.8$, as shown in figure 1.28. In this case:

$$H(z) = \frac{(z - 0.8)}{(z + 0.8)} \tag{1.68}$$

Substituting $\exp(j\Omega)$ for z gives the frequency response:

$$H(\Omega) = \frac{(\exp(j\Omega) - 0.8)}{(\exp(j\Omega) + 0.8)} \tag{1.69}$$

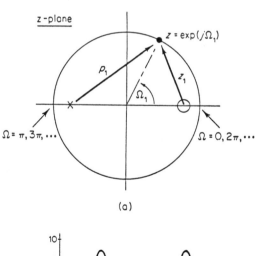

(a)

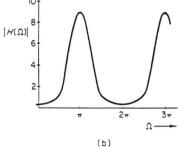

(b)

Figure 1.28   Visualising the frequency response of an LTI processor

We may now use the normal rules of complex arithmetic to interpret $H(\Omega)$ in terms of geometrical vectors drawn in the z-plane.

At a particular value of sinusoidal frequency (say $\Omega = \Omega_1$) the numerator of $H(\Omega)$ may be represented by a *zero vector* Z_1 drawn from the zero to the relevant point on the unit circle. The denominator may be represented by a *pole vector* P_1 drawn from the pole to the same point. The magnitude of $H(\Omega)$ is now given by the length of the zero vector, divided by the length of the pole vector. The phase shift equals the difference between the phase angles of the two vectors (measured with respect to the positive real axis). For the frequency illustrated, we see that $|H(\Omega)|$ must be about 0.6, with a phase shift $\Phi_H(\Omega)$ of about $110° - 35° = 75°$.

We can extend the argument to infer how $|H(\Omega)|$ alters as Ω varies from 0 to 2π. Now $\Omega = 0$ corresponds to the point $z = 1$ on the unit circle. At this frequency the lengths of the zero and pole vectors are 0.2 and 1.8 respectively. Since the transfer function contains no additional gain factor K, the response magnitude is simply $0.2/1.8 = 0.111$. As Ω increases the zero vector grows and the pole vector shortens. At $\Omega = \pi/2$ they are equal in length, giving $|H(\Omega)| = 1$. By the time we reach $\Omega = \pi$, the zero vector has maximum length and the pole vector minimum length. This gives the peak gain of the processor, equal to $1.8/0.2 = 9.0$. As Ω increases further, we continue around the unit circle, reaching our starting point when $\Omega = 2\pi$. The whole cycle then repeats. We therefore generate the periodic frequency response shown in part (b) of the figure. Of course, as always, the response in the range $0 \to \pi$ defines the processor's action on any adequately-sampled original. Therefore this particular pole–zero configuration represents a simple *high-pass* characteristic.

Geometric evaluation of the Fourier Transform in the z-plane can be extended to more complicated processors (or signals), with a greater number of poles and zeros. We draw a vector from each pole and zero to a point on the unit circle representing the sinusoidal frequency of interest. Then:

The *magnitude* of the spectral function equals the *product* of all zero-vector lengths, divided by the *product* of all pole-vector lengths.

The *phase* equals the *sum* of all zero-vector phases, minus the *sum* of all pole-vector phases.

You can probably visualise the effect of any poles or zeros close to the unit circle. As the frequency varies and we move around the unit circle, the spectral magnitude function peaks whenever we pass close to a pole; it goes through a minimum when we pass close to a zero. Note that zeros can occur actually on the unit circle, giving rise to true nulls at the corresponding frequencies. However we have seen that the poles of a stable system are always inside the unit circle, so its response must be finite at all frequencies.

The technique of geometrical evaluation is so useful for visualisation and design that we will end this section with a further example. Let us consider the rather complicated z-Transform already met in equation (1.56). We previously showed how to find its inverse transform using a recursive computer algorithm (see figure 1.25) and drew its poles and zeros in part (b) of figure 1.26. We can now pull together the various threads of our discussion by visualising its magnitude spectrum, and relating it to the time-domain signal.

First, we note that there are zeros at $z = 1$ and $z = \pm j$. Over the frequency range 0 to π, these produce true nulls at $\Omega = 0$ and $\Omega = \pi/2$ (there is also a second-order zero at the origin, but this has no effect on the spectral magnitude). Secondly, there is a complex conjugate pole-pair close to the unit circle at $\Omega = 0.25\pi$ (45°); another at $\Omega = 0.833\pi$ (150°); and a single real pole at $z = -0.8$. The spectrum must therefore be relatively rich in sinusoidal components close to $\Omega = 0.25\pi$, $\Omega = 0.833\pi$, and $\Omega = \pi$. We expect its overall shape to be as shown in figure 1.29.

Now in the time domain, $\Omega = 0.25\pi$ corresponds to a sinusoid with 8 samples per period; $\Omega = 0.833\pi$ has 2.4 samples per period; and $\Omega = \pi$ has 2 samples per period. If you re-examine figure 1.25 very carefully, you may just about be able to detect these three major signal components.

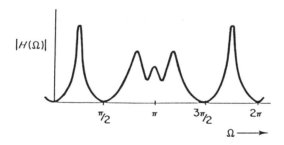

Figure 1.29   Spectral function corresponding to the poles and zeros of part (b) of figure 1.26

Problems

Sections 1.1–1.3

1.1.   Figure P1.1 shows a digital signal $x[n]$. Sketch carefully and label the following signals:

(a) $x[n - 2]$;   (b) $-2x[3 - n]$;   (c) $x[n] + x[1 - n] + u[n]$.

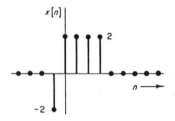

Figure P1.1

1.2. Determine which of the following signals is strictly periodic. If a signal is periodic, find its period.

(a) $x[n] = \sin(\pi n/9)$

(b) $x[n] = \sin(n\pi^2)$

(c) $x[n] = \cos\left(\dfrac{\pi n^2}{15}\right)$

(d) $x[n] = \sin\left(\dfrac{\pi n}{5} + \pi\right) + \cos\left(\dfrac{\pi n}{10} - \pi\right)$.

1.3. $x[n]$ and $y[n]$ are the input and output signals of a digital processor. Which of the following properties are exhibited by each of the processors defined below: linearity; time-invariance; causality; stability; memory?

(a) $y[n] = x[5 - n]$

(b) $y[n] = x[n] x[n - 3]$

(c) $y[n] = x[n] + x[n - 1] + 3x[n - 2]$

(d) $y[n] = 1.5y[n - 1] + x[n - 1]$

(e) $y[n] = nx[n]$.

1.4. Figure P1.4 shows a block diagram of a digital processor. Assuming $y[n] = 0$ for $n < 0$, sketch the output from the processor when the

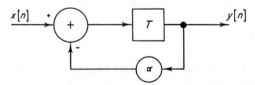

Figure P1.4

input is (a) a unit impulse function, and (b) a unit step function. Assume the coefficient α is between 0 and 1. What would happen if $\alpha > 1$, or $\alpha < -1$?

1.5. Draw a block diagram for a digital processor with the following recurrence formula:

$$y[n] = 1.62y[n - 1] - 0.93y[n - 2] + 0.5x[n] - 0.1x[n - 2]$$

Distinguish clearly between its non-recursive and recursive parts.

1.6. Describe the signals shown in figure P1.6 using sets of weighted, shifted, unit impulse functions.

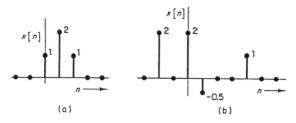

(a)   (b)

Figure P1.6

1.7. Which of the following impulse responses describe causal, stable, LTI processors? Give reasons for your answers.

(a) $h[n] = 3\delta[n - 2] + \delta[n - 4]$

(b) $h[n] = u[n - 3] - u[n + 5]$

(c) $h[n] = \cos(n\pi/8), \quad -1 < n < 20; \quad = 0$ elsewhere

(d) $h[n] = \exp(-0.1n)\, u[n]$

(e) $h[n] = \sin(n)\, \exp(n)\, u[n]$.

1.8. Sketch the first ten terms of the impulse responses of digital filters defined by the following difference equations:

(a) $y[n] = x[n] + x[n - 4] + x[n - 8]$

(b) $y[n] = \displaystyle\sum_{k=0}^{6} (k + 1)\, x[n - k]$.

(c) $y[n] = y[n - 1] + x[n] - x[n - 8]$

(d) $y[n] = y[n - 1] - 0.5y[n - 2] + x[n]$

1.9. Sketch the step responses of the processors defined by the following difference equations:

(a) $y[n] = 0.5y[n-1] + x[n]$

(b) $y[n] = -0.5y[n-1] + x[n]$.

In each case find the value reached by the step response as $n \to \infty$, and hence infer the response of the processor to a unit-height, sampled, dc level.

1.10. Use the graphical interpretation of convolution to find the output $y[n]$ for the input $x[n]$ and impulse response $h[n]$ shown in part (a) of figure P1.10. Sketch $y[n]$ carefully. Repeat the exercise for $x[n]$ and $h[n]$ as shown in part (b) of the figure.

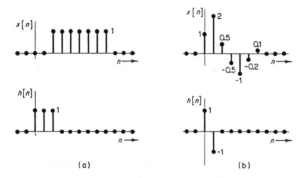

Figure P1.10

1.11. Find a non-recursive difference equation which, from the DSP point of view, is equivalent to the following recursive equation:

(a) $y[n] = y[n-1] + x[n] - x[n-7]$

(b) $y[n] = 0.9y[n-1] + x[n]$.

What is the relative computational economy of the non-recursive and recursive versions of (a)? Why could the non-recursive version of (b) not be exactly implemented in practice?

1.12. Find the impulse response of an overall system formed by cascading two LTI processors with the impulse responses:

$$h_1[n] = 1/n, \quad 0 < n < 4; \quad = 0 \quad \text{elsewhere}$$
$$h_2[n] = n, \quad \quad 0 < n < 4; \quad = 0 \quad \text{elsewhere}$$

Your answer may be expressed as a series of sample values.

Section 1.4

1.13. Find the spectral coefficients a_k for the following periodic digital signals:

(a) $x[n] = 5 + \sin(n\pi/2) + \cos(n\pi/4)$

(b) $x[n] = \cos\left(\dfrac{n\pi}{2} - \dfrac{\pi}{4}\right)$

(c) $x[n] = 2n$ for $0 \leqslant n \leqslant 3$, then repeats.

1.14. Predict the magnitudes and phases of the various spectral coefficients of the periodic signal:

$$x[n] = 1 + \cos\left(\frac{\pi n}{32}\right) + \sin\left(\frac{\pi n}{4}\right), \quad 0 \leqslant n \leqslant 63$$

assuming that it repeats every 64 sample values. Check your predictions with the aid of Computer Program 2 in appendix A.

1.15. Sketch the periodic signal $x[n] = \sin(n\pi/6)$ in the range $0 \leqslant n \leqslant 18$. Use the differentiation property of the Discrete Fourier Series to find the relative magnitude and phase of the first-order difference signal $\{x[n] - x[n-1]\}$. Confirm your results by sketching the latter signal.

1.16. Find an expression for the spectrum $X(\Omega)$ of each of the following aperiodic signals:

(a) $x[n] = \delta[n] + 2\delta[n-1] + \delta[n-2]$

(b) $x[n] = \delta[n+1] - \delta[n-1]$

(c) $x[n] = u[n+3] - u[n-4]$.

1.17. A simple high-pass filter has the recurrence formula;

$$y[n] = -0.9y[n-1] + 0.1x[n]$$

Find an expression for the frequency response $H(\Omega)$, and sketch its magnitude over the range $0 \leqslant \Omega \leqslant \pi$. What is the value of $|H(\Omega)|$ at (a) $\Omega = 0$, and (b) $\Omega = \pi$?

1.18. A bandpass filter is shown in figure P1.18. Find an expression for its frequency response magnitude $|H(\Omega)|$, and sketch the function in the range $0 \leqslant \Omega \leqslant \pi$.

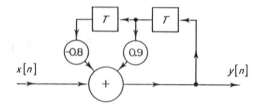

Figure P1.18

Section 1.5

1.19. Expand the following z-Transforms as power series in z^{-1}, and write down their first five sample values (starting at $n = 0$):

(a) $X(z) = \dfrac{1}{(z - 0.5)}$

(b) $X(z) = \dfrac{z}{(z + 1.1)}$

(c) $X(z) = \dfrac{(z + 1)}{(z - 1)}$.

1.20. A signal $x[n]$ begins at $n = 0$ and has six finite sample values:

$$1, 2, 3, 1, -1, 1$$

It forms the input to an LTI processor whose impulse response $h[n]$ begins at $n = 0$ and has three finite sample values:

$$1, 1, 1$$

Convolve $x[n]$ with $h[n]$ to find the output signal $y[n]$. Check that the z-Transform of $y[n]$ equals the product of the transforms of $x[n]$ and $h[n]$.

1.21. Using the table of z-Transforms in appendix B, and partial fraction expansions if necessary, find the signals corresponding to the following z-Transforms;

(a) $X(z) = \dfrac{0.5z}{z^2 - z + 0.5}$

(b) $X(z) = \dfrac{(z - 0.5)}{z(z - 0.8)(z - 1)}$.

1.22. Write computer programs to estimate and plot the inverse z-Transforms of the following functions:

(a) the function in problem **1.21**(b)

(b) $X(z) = \dfrac{(z + 1)(z^2 + 1.5z + 0.9)}{(z + 0.7)(z^2 - 1.6z + 0.95)}$.

1.23. Find the z-plane poles and zeros of the following transfer functions. Which, if any, represent unstable or non-causal processors?

(a) $H(z) = \dfrac{z^2 - z - 2}{z^2 - 1.3z + 0.4}$

(b) $H(z) = \dfrac{z^2 - z + 1}{z^2 + 1}$

(c) $H(z) = \dfrac{z^3 - z^2 + z - 1}{z^2 - 0.25}$

(d) $H(z) = \dfrac{z^9 - 1}{(z - 1)z^8}$.

1.24. Using table B.3 in appendix B, find the signals corresponding to the pole–zero configurations shown in figure P1.24.

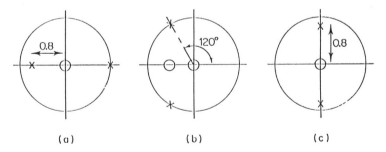

(a)   (b)   (c)

Figure P1.24

1.25. Using the technique of geometrical evaluation of the Fourier Transform in the z-plane, make rough sketches of the spectral magnitude characteristics of signals with the pole–zero configurations shown in figure P1.25.

If the pole–zero configurations refer to LTI filters, rather than signals, what type of filter does each represent?

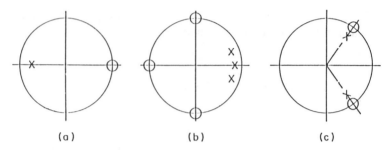

(a)   (b)   (c)

Figure P1.25

1.26. A second-order filter has the difference equation;

$$y[n] = \alpha y[n-1] - \beta y[n-2] + x[n]$$

What ranges of the coefficients α and β are possible if the filter is to be stable (and therefore usable)? If β is close to unity, approximately what value of α will give:

(a) a passband centred at $\Omega = \pi/3$

(b) a passband centred at $\Omega = 2\pi/3$?

2 Digital Filter Design

In this chapter we outline some of the best-known methods for designing non-recursive and recursive digital filters. Although almost any DSP algorithm or processor can reasonably be described as a 'filter', the term is commonly reserved for processors which transmit (or reject) well-defined frequency ranges. Typical, idealised, magnitude characteristics of four digital filter categories are shown in figure 2.1. Remember that although the frequency response of a digital processor is always repetitive in form, its performance over the range $0 \leqslant \Omega \leqslant \pi$ defines the filtering action on any adequately-sampled signal. For example, a filter having a response peak at $\Omega = \pi$ (and therefore also at $\Omega = 3\pi, 5\pi, \ldots$) is described as 'high pass'.

We emphasise spectral magnitude functions in this chapter, but there are other ways of specifying a digital filter. For example, there is a class of processors known as *all-pass*, with flat magnitude responses and phase characteristics which vary with frequency in some desired manner. Alternatively, we may be interested in a particular form of impulse or step response; or we may need to optimise the detection of a signal in the presence of noise (a topic introduced in chapter 5). A wide variety of design techniques is available for tackling such problems. It is therefore

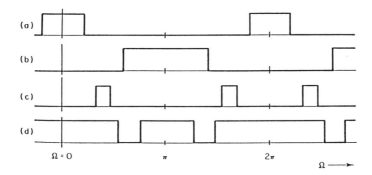

Figure 2.1 Idealised digital filter frequency responses: (a) low-pass, (b) high-pass, (c) bandpass and (d) bandstop

53

important to realise that our account of digital filter design in this chapter is both selective and introductory.

2.1   Non-recursive filters

2.1.1   Introduction

The general form of difference equation for a causal LTI processor (see also equation (1.42)) is given by

$$\sum_{k=0}^{N} a_k \, y[n - k] = \sum_{k=0}^{M} b_k x[n - k] \qquad (2.1)$$

In the case of a non-recursive filter the present output sample value depends only on present and previous inputs, so the difference equation reduces to

$$y[n] = \sum_{k=0}^{M} b_k x[n - k] \qquad (2.2)$$

Such a filter implements the convolution sum directly, and the multiplier coefficients b_k are simply equal to successive terms in its impulse response. This is shown by figure 2.2. Since the number of coefficients must be finite, a practical non-recursive filter is often referred to as *FIR (finite impulse response)*.

The transfer function and frequency response corresponding to equation (2.2) are respectively

$$H(z) = \sum_{k=0}^{M} b_k z^{-k} \qquad (2.3)$$

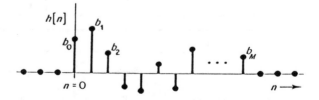

Figure 2.2   Impulse response coefficients for a non-recursive filter

and

$$H(\Omega) = \sum_{k=0}^{M} b_k \exp(-jk\Omega) \tag{2.4}$$

The art of designing non-recursive filters is to achieve acceptable performance using as few coefficients b_k as possible. Practical filters typically
need between (say) 10 and 150 coefficients. This makes them slower in
operation than most recursive designs. However there are two compensat-
ing advantages. Firstly, a non-recursive filter is inherently stable, since it
does not involve feedback. And secondly, its impulse response can easily
be made symmetrical in form, leading to a pure linear-phase characteristic
with no phase distortion.

The last point is illustrated by figure 2.3. Suppose we start with a
non-causal impulse response, symmetrical about $n = 0$, as shown in part
(a). The corresponding frequency response is

$$H(\Omega) = \sum_{k=-M}^{M} b_k \exp(-jk\Omega)$$

$$= b_0 + 2b_1 \cos\Omega + 2b_2 \cos 2\Omega + \ldots + 2b_M \cos M\Omega$$

$$= b_0 + 2 \sum_{k=1}^{M} b_k \cos k\Omega \tag{2.5}$$

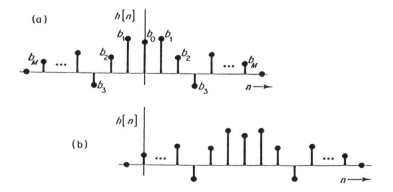

Figure 2.3 Impulse responses giving (a) zero-phase, and (b) linear-phase
characteristics

$H(\Omega)$ is a real function of Ω, implying a zero-phase filter with no phase shift at any frequency. To make the filter causal we shift $h[n]$ by M sampling intervals as shown in part (b) of the figure. The effect is to delay the output by the same amount, converting the zero-phase characteristic into a pure linear-phase one. The magnitude of the frequency response is unaffected.

Although non-recursive filters do not *have* to display linear-phase characteristics, the majority of practical designs take advantage of the possibility – which is not available in recursive filters based upon z-plane poles.

One of the simplest non-recursive filters is the moving-average type with all its coefficients b_k equal. As figures 1.1 and 1.15 have already demonstrated, its low-pass or smoothing action is adequate in some relatively undemanding applications. However the frequency response of such a filter is a poor approximation to the ideal characteristic of figure 2.1, having an ill-defined main passband lobe and substantial unwanted sidelobes (in fact, the response is close to a sin x/x, or sinc, function). This difficulty emphasises the fact that, in most cases, we need to approach the design problem 'the other way round'. In other words we need to be able to define the coefficients of a digital filter which best approximates a *specified* frequency response. One of the most widely used techniques is based on discrete-time Fourier transformation, and is known as the *Fourier Transform method*.

2.1.2 The Fourier Transform method

The Fourier Transform method is very flexible, and can in principle be used to design a non-recursive filter with any form of frequency response. Consider the inverse transform, given by equation (1.36), but rewritten to describe an LTI processor rather than a signal:

$$h[n] = \frac{1}{2\pi} \int_{2\pi} H(\Omega) \exp(\mathrm{j}\Omega n) \, \mathrm{d}\Omega \tag{2.6}$$

If we start with a desired frequency response $H(\Omega)$, the equation shows how to derive the corresponding impulse response $h[n]$. The sample values of $h[n]$ equal the required multiplier coefficients b_k for our non-recursive filter.

The approach is conceptually straightforward, but there are two potential difficulties in practice. First, the integral in equation (2.6) may not be easy to solve – especially if $H(\Omega)$ has a complicated form. We will therefore concentrate on the type of idealised filter magnitude characteristics already illustrated by figure 2.1.

The second difficulty concerns the number of terms in $h[n]$. Our choice of $H(\Omega)$ may result in an impulse response with a great many terms, giving an uneconomic filter. We shall see later that there are ways around this problem, involving a compromise between the filter's time- and frequency-domain performance.

Let us start by considering the ideal low-pass filter characteristic of figure 2.4. This is the desired $H(\Omega)$. We have defined it over the range $\Omega = -\pi$ to π, rather than 0 to 2π, to simplify the integral in equation (2.6). We begin by assuming a zero-phase processor for which $H(\Omega)$ is real. Thus

$$h[n] = \frac{1}{2\pi} \int_{-\pi}^{\pi} H(\Omega) \exp(j\Omega n) \, d\Omega$$

$$= \frac{1}{2\pi} \int_{-\Omega_1}^{\Omega_1} 1.\exp(j\Omega n) \, d\Omega = \frac{1}{2\pi} \left[\frac{\exp(j\Omega n)}{jn} \right]_{-\Omega_1}^{\Omega_1}$$

$$= \frac{1}{2\pi jn} \{\exp(j\Omega_1 n) - \exp(-j\Omega_1 n)\}$$

Hence

$$h[n] = \frac{1}{n\pi} \sin n\Omega_1 = \frac{\Omega_1}{\pi} \text{sinc}(n\Omega_1) \tag{2.7}$$

Such sinc functions often arise in linear signal and system theory. Generally speaking, a 'rectangular pulse' in either the time- or frequency-domain transforms into a sinc function in the other domain. We previously noted that a simple low-pass moving-average filter, with a 'rectangular' impulse response, has a sinc form of frequency response. We are now specifying an ideal 'rectangular' or 'brickwall' frequency response, so we get an impulse response whose terms follow a sinc envelope.

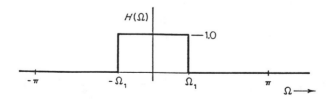

Figure 2.4   An ideal low-pass filter characteristic

As a specific example, let us find and sketch the impulse response of an ideal, zero-phase, low-pass filter with a cut-off frequency $\Omega_1 = \pi/2$. Using equation (2.7), we have

$$h[n] = \frac{1}{n\pi} \sin\left(\frac{n\pi}{2}\right) \tag{2.8}$$

The coefficient $h[0]$ is a little awkward to find, because the numerator and denominator are both zero. Resorting to l'Hospital's rule we obtain:

$$h[0] = \left. \frac{\dfrac{d}{dn}\left\{\sin\dfrac{n\pi}{2}\right\}}{\dfrac{d}{dn}\{n\pi\}} \right|_{n=0} = \left. \frac{\dfrac{\pi}{2}\cos\dfrac{n\pi}{2}}{\pi} \right|_{n=0} = 0.5 \tag{2.9}$$

Other values are readily calculated, and the resulting impulse response is drawn over the range $-16 \leqslant n \leqslant 16$ in figure 2.5.

Although $h[n]$ decays to either side of $n = 0$, it theoretically continues for ever in both directions. This reflects a general antithesis between band limitation and time limitation: since we have chosen a frequency response with an infinitely sharp cut-off, the time-domain response continues for ever. To realise such a filter we must clearly limit, or *truncate*, the impulse response in some way. The obvious approach (although, as we shall see later, not necessarily the best one) is to ignore the small sample values in its 'tails'. We can then shift $h[n]$ to begin at $n = 0$, giving a causal filter with pure linear-phase characteristics.

There is a compromise to be made here. The more samples of $h[n]$ we include, the closer we get to the desired form of $H(\Omega)$; but the less economic the filter becomes. In practice we must settle for an *approximation* to the ideal frequency response.

So far we have concentrated on filters with low-pass characteristics. However it is a relatively simple matter to generate equivalent high-pass or

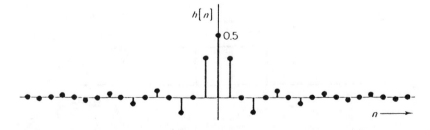

Figure 2.5   Impulse response of an ideal, zero-phase, low-pass filter

bandpass designs. The most obvious approach is to inverse-transform the desired frequency response using equation (2.6), as before. But it is also worth noting that we can derive a bandpass or high-pass filter by multiplying, or *modulating*, the low-pass impulse response $h[n]$ with a cosine signal at the desired centre frequency. Such time-domain multiplication is equivalent to frequency-domain convolution, and has the effect of shifting the low-pass characteristic bodily along the frequency axis. Combining this idea with equation (2.7), the impulse response coefficients of an ideal filter with centre-frequency Ω_0 and bandwidth $2\Omega_1$ are given by

$$h[n] = \frac{1}{n\pi} \sin(n\Omega_1) \cos(n\Omega_0) \tag{2.10}$$

Substituting the values of $h[n]$ for the coefficients b_k in equation (2.5), we also have:

$$H(\Omega) = \frac{\Omega_1}{\pi} + 2 \sum_{k=1}^{\infty} h[k] \cos(k\Omega) \tag{2.11}$$

In practice we will truncate the impulse response to $(2M + 1)$ terms – that is, $h[0]$ and M terms to either side of it – and shift it to begin at $n = 0$. The frequency response magnitude characteristic is then:

$$|H(\Omega)| = \frac{\Omega_1}{\pi} + 2 \sum_{k=1}^{M} h[k] \cos(k\Omega) \tag{2.12}$$

It is quite straightforward to compute $h[n]$ and $|H(\Omega)|$ using equations (2.10) and (2.12). Figure 2.6 shows three examples of bandpass filter responses, all with centre-frequency $\Omega_0 = \pi/3$ and bandwidth $2\Omega_1 = \pi/6$, but with different values of the parameter M. The corresponding impulse responses are truncated to 21 terms ($M = 10$), 51 terms ($M = 25$), and 151 terms ($M = 75$), giving three different approximations to the ideal, rectangular, frequency response. Note how the 'goodness of fit' improves as M increases.

What is the nature of the approximation involved in the foregoing designs? In fact it may be shown that the Fourier Transform method gives the best approximation in a *least-squares* sense. Thus suppose we have specified a desired frequency response $H_D(\Omega)$, but after impulse response truncation we get an actual frequency response $H_A(\Omega)$. Let us define the overall error between desired and actual responses as

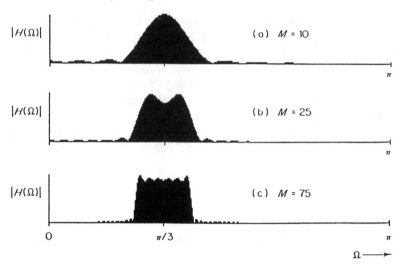

Figure 2.6   Frequency responses of three linear-phase bandpass filters, obtained by truncating the 'ideal' impulse response (*abscissa: 320 samples*)

$$e = \int_{2\pi} |H_D(\Omega) - H_A(\Omega)|^2 \, d\Omega \qquad (2.13)$$

That is, we take account of the squared-magnitude of the difference between desired and actual responses over one complete period in the frequency domain. All frequencies are treated equally. It turns out that, for a given number of impulse response coefficients, the Fourier Transform method minimises the value of e. Those of you familiar with continuous-time Fourier Analysis will recall that such least-squares approximation is one of its central features.

Minimisation of e is a valuable design criterion, but it is by no means the only possible one. For example, we may be more interested in controlling the sidelobe levels of a filter, or in achieving a sharp transition between passband and stopband. To understand such possibilities we must consider the question of truncation from a more general point of view, and introduce the techniques of *windowing*.

2.1.3 Window functions

When we truncate an infinite-length impulse response, we effectively multiply it by a *rectangular window*. This is illustrated in figure 2.7. Part (a) represents the impulse response $h_d[n]$ which is the inverse transform of the

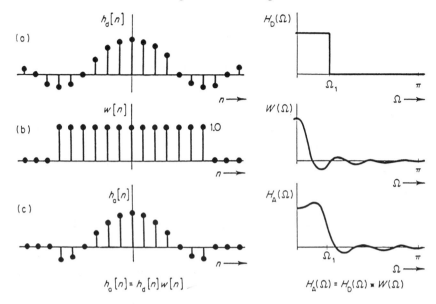

Figure 2.7   Windowing in the time and frequency domains

ideal, or desired, frequency response $H_D(\Omega)$. Multiplication by the window function $w[n]$ in part (b) gives the truncated impulse response $h_a[n]$ in part (c). Clearly, by altering the length of $w[n]$ we can control the number of terms in $h_a[n]$.

Note that it is convenient at this stage to treat all time functions as symmetrical about $n = 0$, giving spectral functions which are real (zero-phase). Later, we can easily shift the truncated impulse response forward to begin at $n = 0$, defining a causal, linear-phase filter.

The modulation property of the Fourier Transform tells us that time-domain multiplication is equivalent to frequency-domain convolution. Therefore the above windowing process must produce an actual frequency response $H_A(\Omega)$ which is the convolution of $H_D(\Omega)$ with the spectrum of the window $W(\Omega)$. We see this on the right-hand side of the figure. The spectrum of a rectangular window tends to the $\sin x/x$, or sinc, form. Its convolution with $H_D(\Omega)$ gives an *approximation* to the desired frequency response containing a number of fluctuations or *ripples*. These distort the shape of the passband, and produce unwanted *sidelobes*.

If we increase the length of the rectangular window, its spectrum becomes narrower. The ripples in $H_A(\Omega)$ bunch more closely around the nominal cut-off frequency Ω_1. Also, the transition from passband to stopband becomes sharper (you may like to refer back to figure 2.6, which shows such effects clearly). However the window spectrum is still of sinc form, so lengthening the window does not reduce the ripple *magnitudes*.

J. W. Gibbs showed in about 1900 that the maximum ripple in the region of a sudden transition is approximately 9 per cent, regardless of window length. The effect is known as the *Gibbs' phenomenon*.

In general, we conclude that the size and shape of the ripples in $H_A(\Omega)$ depend on the form of $W(\Omega)$. If $W(\Omega)$ were a frequency-domain impulse, then the actual and desired frequency responses would be identical. This might seem the ideal situation, but of course we could not attain it in practice: an impulse in the frequency domain implies an infinitely long time window, so we would not be truncating at all! It is therefore clear that a compromise is required between time- and frequency-domain performance.

To discuss this question properly we should look more carefully at the spectral ripples, or sidelobes, of the rectangular window. Figure 2.8 shows the spectra of two such windows, plotted to decibel (dB) scales. We see that the first sidelobe is about 13.5 dB down on the main lobe, and that there are many sidelobes above about −30 dB. A window with this sidelobe performance is unsuitable for most digital filtering applications. The basic reason for the poor sidelobe levels is that the window 'chops off' suddenly in the time domain, leading to spreading in the frequency domain. Intuitively, we may expect that a more 'gentle' window function, which tapers towards its edges, will give better results.

However we must be careful not to dismiss the rectangular window completely. As noted in the previous section, it gives the best approxima-

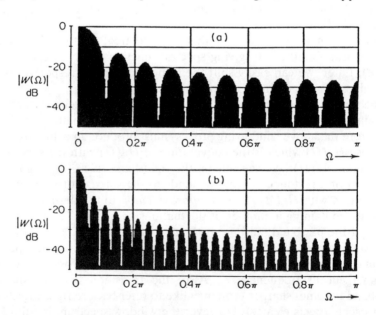

Figure 2.8   Spectra of rectangular windows with (a) 21 terms, and (b) 51 terms (*abscissa: 320 samples*)

tion to the desired frequency response in a least-squares sense. If we choose another form of window, we will have to forfeit this advantage. But we should be able to trade it against improved ripple and sidelobe performance.

The triangular, or *Bartlett*, window at the top of figure 2.9 offers a simple form of tapering. Transformed into the frequency domain, it produces sidelobe levels with decibel values about half those of a rectangular window. However a disadvantage is that, for a given window length, its main spectral lobe is twice as wide as that of a rectangular window. Convolved with a desired frequency response $H_D(\Omega)$, this causes a broadening of the transition region between passband and stopband. Part (b) of the figure shows the spectrum of a 41-term triangular window ($M = 20$).

Many improved window functions have been devised over the years. Of these *von Hann* and especially *Hamming* windows have been widely used by DSP designers. Both have a main spectral lobe similar to that of a triangular window, but offer considerably smaller sidelobe levels.

A von Hann window, also referred to as a *Hanning* window, with ($2M + 1$) terms is defined by:

$$w[n] = 0.5 + 0.5 \cos\left(\frac{n\pi}{M + 1}\right), \quad -M \leq n \leq M$$

$$= 0 \qquad\qquad \text{elsewhere} \qquad\qquad (2.14)$$

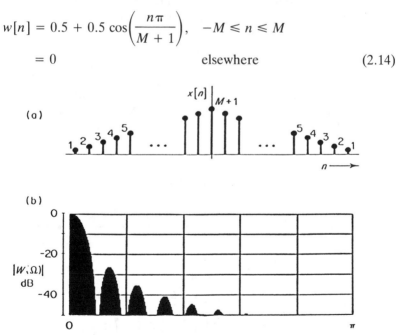

Figure 2.9   (a) A triangular function, and (b) the spectrum of a 41-term triangular window (*abscissa: 320 samples*)

An example with 21 terms ($M = 10$) is shown in part (a) of figure 2.10. Note that the 'raised cosine' shape gives a smoother tapering action than the triangular window. We shall investigate its spectrum a little later.

By altering the relative proportions of the dc and cosine components in the von Hann window, R. W. Hamming found that he could further improve sidelobe levels. The Hamming window is defined as:

$$w[n] = 0.54 + 0.46 \cos\left(\frac{n\pi}{M}\right), \quad -M \leq n \leq M$$

$$= 0 \qquad \qquad \text{elsewhere} \qquad (2.15)$$

(Actually the optimum proportions are slightly dependent on the value of M. Values of 0.54 and 0.46 are usually quoted, being very close to optimum for M greater than about 10.) A 21-term Hamming window is illustrated in part (b) of the figure.

Figure 2.11 shows the spectra of von Hann and Hamming windows with 51 terms ($M = 25$). We have also included a plot for a 51-term triangular window, to aid comparison. Whereas the triangular function gives a first sidelobe level of about -27 dB, the von Hann window has a level of about -32 dB with subsequent sidelobes below -40 dB. The Hamming window is best of all, with all its sidelobes below -40 dB. If you look very carefully you will see that the main lobes of the von Hann and Hamming windows are slightly wider than that of the triangular window. However, this is a small price to pay for the much improved sidelobe performance.

Our next computer program, listed in appendix A, brings together most of the ideas covered in this chapter so far. Computer Program 3 may be used to design a wide range of non-recursive digital filters based on

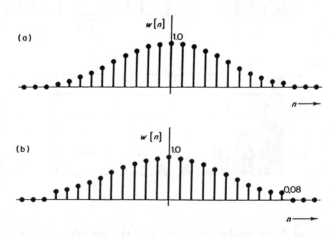

Figure 2.10   21-term von Hann and Hamming windows

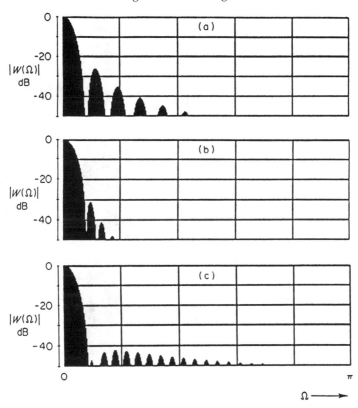

Figure 2.11 Spectra of 51-term windows: (a) triangular, (b) von Hann and (c) Hamming (*abscissa: 320 samples*)

rectangular, von Hann, or Hamming truncation windows. It requests information on filter centre-frequency, bandwidth, window length, and window type (note that the bandwidth of a low-pass or high-pass design must be entered as twice its value in the range $0 \leqslant \Omega \leqslant \pi$). It produces a dB plot of the filter's frequency response, and prints out the impulse response values, scaled to give unity peak gain (0 dB). The impulse response is considered to be symmetrical about $n = 0$, and values $h[0]$ (the central one) to $h[M]$ (one of the 'tails') are given. To make the impulse response causal, its 'other half' must be added, and it must be shifted to begin at $n = 0$.

Figure 2.12 shows some typical frequency response plots, emphasising the differences caused by the various windows. The specification is for a bandpass filter with centre-frequency $\Omega = 2\pi/3$ (120°) and bandwidth $\pi/18$ (10°), having a 51-term impulse response ($M = 25$). Part (a) shows the rectangular window version of the filter. Its largest sidelobe level of about

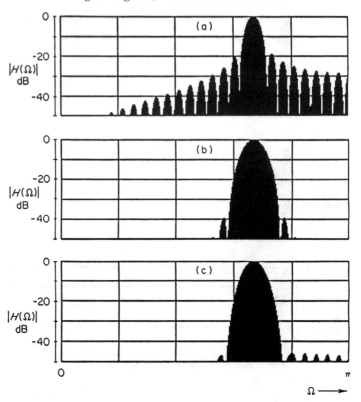

Figure 2.12   Frequency responses of three non-recursive bandpass filters
designed by the window method (*abscissa: 320 samples*)

−20 dB is an example of the Gibbs phenomenon, and is the result of
convolving the window spectrum (with its first sidelobe level of about
−13.5 dB) with the rectangular spectrum of the 'desired' filter.

Part (b) of the figure illustrates the von Hann version of the filter.
Sidelobes are reduced at the expense of a broader main lobe. Part (c)
shows the Hamming version, with all sidelobes better than about −46 dB.

A disadvantage of the von Hann and Hamming filters is that their main
lobes are a lot wider than the desired value. To some extent we could
narrow them by requesting a smaller bandwidth in the first place. However
a limit is soon reached, because a filter's main lobe cannot be narrower
than that of its truncation window. Further bandwidth reduction can only
be achieved by accepting a longer window (that is, a greater value of *M*).

We end this section with a brief mention of another, rather more
complicated, window function which is often used in non-recursive filter
design – the *Kaiser* window.

We start by noting that the windows described so far all have fixed shapes, offering a particular trade-off between main lobe width and sidelobe levels. It was the major contribution of J. F. Kaiser to suggest a variable window, specified in terms of a Bessel function, in which the trade-off can be adjusted by the DSP designer. The overall approach is summarised by figure 2.13, which shows an ideal filter characteristic $H_D(\Omega)$, together with an acceptable ripple level $\pm\delta$ in both passband and stopband, and an acceptable transition width Δ. The aim is to produce an actual filter characteristic $H_A(\Omega)$ which avoids the shaded regions of the figure, using as few impulse response terms as possible. Kaiser was able to relate ripple level and transition width to the length and shape of the required window, and gave empirical formulae for its design. If you are interested in this type of filter, you will find it described in references 4 and 11 given in the Bibliography at the end of this book.

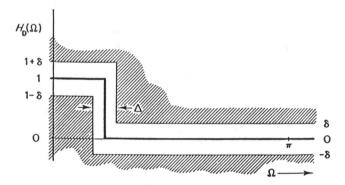

Figure 2.13   Specifying the design of a Kaiser-window filter

2.1.4 Equiripple filters

We have seen in the previous sections that practical filter design is essentially an approximation problem. Starting with a desired form of frequency response, we try to approximate it to an acceptable degree of accuracy. The Fourier design method uses various window functions to give different compromises between the width of the transition band, and the size of ripples and sidelobes.

If you refer back to actual frequency responses obtained with different windows – for example, figures 2.6 and 2.12 – you will see that the largest ripples and sidelobes generally occur near the transition from passband to stopband. As we move away from the transition region, the error between the desired and actual responses becomes smaller. This raises the interesting possibility that, if the error can be distributed more equally over the range $0 \leqslant \Omega \leqslant \pi$, we may achieve a better overall compromise between ripple levels, transition bandwidth and filter order. Of course, such a compromise will not produce the best approximation in the least-squares sense – this is only achieved by the Fourier method with a rectangular window. But it should offer other features which are valuable to the DSP designer.

Equiripple filters exploit the above possibility. The aim is to find an approximation giving acceptable levels of ripple throughout the passband and stopband – rather than just meeting the specification at one frequency, and greatly exceeding it elsewhere.

Non-recursive filters of this type are designed in quite a different way from the filters we have met previously. Essentially, the frequency response function $H(\Omega)$ is examined for local maxima and minima (*extrema*), corresponding to passband and stopband ripples. Using an iterative algorithm, the filter is then adjusted to meet the equiripple specification. Our aim here is simply to summarise the approach, so that if you meet non-recursive equiripple filters later you will appreciate their main features. Further theoretical background, plus a useful list of research references, is given in the book by Oppenheim and Schafer (see reference 5 in the Bibliography at the end of this book).

Figure 2.14 illustrates the specification for a low-pass equiripple filter. In the passband ($0 \leq \Omega \leq \Omega_p$), the acceptable level of ripple is $\pm\delta_1$; in the stopband ($\Omega_s \leq \Omega \leq \pi$), the acceptable ripple is $\pm\delta_2$. The width of the transition band is ($\Omega_s - \Omega_p$). The figure also shows a typical filter response which just meets the specification (note that the number of ripples is directly related to the order of the filter, and hence to the length of its impulse response). Ripple peaks and troughs occur at $\Omega_1, \Omega_2, \Omega_3, \ldots$. In most respects the tolerance scheme is like that of a Kaiser window filter

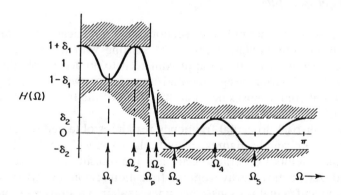

Figure 2.14   Specifying the design of an equiripple low-pass filter

(see figure 2.13); but it has the added flexibility of allowing different ripple levels in passband and stopband.

As with other non-recursive techniques, equiripple design normally starts by assuming an even impulse response, symmetric about $n = 0$. This gives zero-phase characteristics. The impulse response can then be shifted forward to begin at $n = 0$, producing a causal filter with pure linear-phase. As we showed at the start of this chapter, the frequency response of a zero-phase non-recursive filter takes the general form (see equation 2.5):

$$H(\Omega) = \sum_{k=-M}^{M} b_k \exp(-jk\Omega) = b_0 + 2\sum_{k=1}^{M} b_k \cos k\Omega \tag{2.16}$$

where the coefficients b_k equal the terms of the filter's impulse response $h[n]$. Hence we may also write:

$$H(\Omega) = h[0] + 2\sum_{k=1}^{M} h[k] \cos k\Omega \tag{2.17}$$

Now a term $\cos k\Omega$ can always be expressed as a sum of powers of $\cos\Omega$. Therefore equation (2.17) can be recast in the form

$$H(\Omega) = \sum_{k=0}^{M} c_k (\cos \Omega)^k \tag{2.18}$$

where the coefficients c_k are related to the impulse response values. This shows that the frequency response $H(\Omega)$ of such a filter can be written as an Mth-order trigonometric polynomial. We conclude that it can display up to $(M - 1)$ local extrema within the range $0 < \Omega < \pi$, corresponding to ripple peaks and troughs. Furthermore, differentiating equation (2.18) with respect to Ω we obtain:

$$H'(\Omega) = \frac{dH(\Omega)}{d\Omega} = -\sin\Omega \sum_{k=1}^{M} kc_k(\cos\Omega)^{k-1} \tag{2.19}$$

Since $\sin\Omega$ is zero when $\Omega = 0$ and π, there must be a maximum or minimum at both these frequencies. Hence there can be, at most, $(M + 1)$ extrema over the range $0 \leqslant \Omega \leqslant \pi$. In general, the extrema are not divided equally between passband and stopband.

Not surprisingly the design parameters M, δ_1, δ_2, Ω_p and Ω_s interact, and cannot all be independently specified. Two main approaches were developed in the early 1970s:

Hermann and Schuessler specified the parameters M, δ_1 and δ_2, allowing Ω_p and Ω_s to vary. They showed that the equiripple behaviour of figure 2.14 could be expressed by a set of non-linear equations. The difficulty of solving the equations for large values of M led Hofstetter, Oppenheim and Siegel to develop an iterative algorithm for finding a trigonometric polynomial with the required properties.

Parks and McClellan chose to specify M, Ω_p, Ω_s and the ripple ratio δ_1/δ_2, while allowing the actual value of δ_1 to vary. Their approach has the advantage that the transition bandwidth – an important feature of most practical designs – is properly controlled. The design problem was shown to reduce to a so-called Chebyshev approximation over disjoint sets.

The approach of Parks and McClellan is widely used, so we will say a few words about it. Basically, they showed that equiripple approximations giving optimum error performance in passband and stopband must display either $(M + 2)$ or $(M + 3)$ *alternations* of the error function over the range $0 \leqslant \Omega \leqslant \pi$. The alternations represent successive reversals of the peak error (between desired and actual responses), at the maximum permitted level.

Two typical examples are shown in figure 2.15, for the case $M = 7$ (a filter with 15 impulse response terms). The alternations are marked with dots. In part (a) of the figure there are $M + 3 = 10$ alternations – the maximum number possible. Note that the alternations at Ω_p and Ω_s are not local extrema of $H(\Omega)$. The other 8 alternations, one of which occurs at

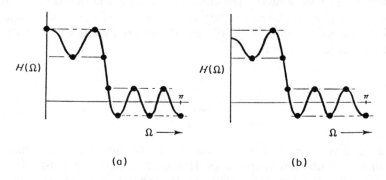

(a)   (b)

Figure 2.15   Parks–McClellan equiripple filters

$\Omega = 0$ and one at $\Omega = \pi$, are local extrema. They correspond to the $(M + 1)$ possible extrema of $H(\Omega)$. This form of response was named *extraripple* by Parks and McClellan, because it has one more alternation than the $(M + 2)$ demanded for optimum error performance.

Part (b) of the figure illustrates another case, this time with just $(M + 2)$ alternations. As usual, $H(\Omega)$ displays local extrema at $\Omega = 0$ and $\Omega = \pi$; but the former is not an alternation, because it does not reach the permitted ripple level. Two other cases with $(M + 2)$ alternations, not illustrated here, are also possible. In one, the ripple peak at $\Omega = 0$ is an alternation, but that at $\Omega = \pi$ is not. In the other case, the ripple peaks at both $\Omega = 0$ and $\Omega = \pi$ are alternations, but there is one less intermediate ripple in the response.

We therefore see that there are several minor variations of Parks–McClellan filters, all of which offer optimum equiripple performance. Such filters give the sharpest passband–stopband transition for specified ripple levels and filter order. It is perhaps unlikely that you will ever have to design one in detail yourself; but you are quite likely to meet them as part of a standard DSP software package.

2.2 Recursive filters

2.2.1 Introduction

A recursive filter involves *feedback*. In other words, each of its output values is calculated using one or more previous outputs, as well as inputs. From the DSP point of view, the great advantage is computational economy. A filter characteristic requiring (say) 100 or more coefficients in a non-recursive realisation can often be obtained using just a few recursive coefficients. However there are two potential disadvantages. First, a recursive filter may become unstable if its feedback coefficients are chosen badly. Secondly, recursive designs cannot generally provide the linear-phase responses so readily achieved by non-recursive methods.

In most cases a recursive filter has an impulse response which theoretically continues for ever. It is therefore referred to as an *infinite impulse response*, or *IIR*, filter. Assuming it is causal, so that the impulse response $h[n] = 0$ for $n < 0$, it follows that $h[n]$ cannot be symmetrical in form. Therefore the filter cannot display pure linear-phase characteristics.

Whereas the transfer function of a non-recursive filter has only z-plane zeros, a recursive design uses one or more strategically placed z-plane poles. In general, we may write its transfer function and difference equation as:

$$H(z) = \frac{\displaystyle\sum_{k=0}^{M} b_k z^{-k}}{\displaystyle\sum_{k=0}^{N} a_k z^{-k}} \qquad (2.20)$$

and

$$a_0\, y[n] + a_1 y[n-1] + \ldots a_N y[n-N] = b_0 x[n] + b_1 x[n-1]$$
$$+ \ldots b_M x[n-M] \qquad (2.21)$$

where $N > 0$ and $M \geqslant 0$. Factorising the numerator and denominator polynomials of equation (2.20), we obtain the pole–zero description of the filter (as in equation (1.60)):

$$H(z) = \frac{K(z - z_1)(z - z_2)(z - z_3) \ldots}{(z - p_1)(z - p_2)(z - p_3) \ldots} \qquad (2.22)$$

The art of designing a recursive filter is to approximate a desired performance – usually specified in terms of a frequency response characteristic – using as few poles and zeros as possible.

It is a straightforward matter to compute the frequency response $H(\Omega)$ corresponding to equation (2.22), by substituting $\exp(j\Omega)$ for z. The basic reason why recursive techniques are so powerful is that we have separate control over the numerator and denominator of $H(\Omega)$. In particular, we can produce sharp response peaks by arranging that the magnitude of the denominator becomes small at the desired frequencies. This is done by placing a z-plane pole, or poles, close to the unit circle.

Perhaps the most obvious approach is to use the technique of geometrical evaluation of the Fourier Transform in the z-plane, described in section 1.5.2, to choose z-plane pole and zero locations intuitively. We can then write down the difference equation, and compute the frequency response. The method is rather 'hit-or-miss', but it can be quite effective for relatively undemanding applications (including the EMG notch filter described in section 1.1). You will find a number of filters of this type described in reference 4 in the Bibliography at the end of this book.

A less obvious, but much more effective, approach is to use the extensive knowledge on analog filter design, built up over the past sixty or seventy years, to design equivalent digital filters. Since our approach in this book is essentially digital, we do not wish to discuss analog filters in any detail. Instead we will try to summarise their links with certain well-known types of recursive digital filter, setting the scene with some general remarks.

We start by noting that the *Laplace Transform* plays a similar role in analog signal and systems theory to that of the z-Transform in the digital case. For example, an analog LTI filter can always be described by a frequency-domain transfer function of the general form

$$H(s) = \frac{K(s - z_1)(s - z_2)(s - z_3) \cdots}{(s - p_1)(s - p_2)(s - p_3) \cdots} \tag{2.23}$$

where s is the Laplace variable and K is a constant, or gain, factor. Apart from this factor the filter may be characterised by its poles $p_1, p_2, p_3 \cdots$, and its zeros $z_1, z_2, z_3 \cdots$, which can be plotted in the complex s-plane.

Although the form of equation (2.23) is identical to that describing the transfer function $H(z)$ of a digital processor, the variable s is *not* the same as the variable z. For example, the frequency response of a digital filter is found by making the substitution $\exp(j\Omega)$ for z; but the equivalent substitution in the analog case is $j\omega$ for s, where ω is the angular frequency in radians per second. It follows that the imaginary axis in the s-plane ($s = j\omega$) maps into the unit circle in the z-plane, and that the interpretation of pole–zero locations is different in the two cases. Another essential difference is that the frequency response of an analog filter is not a periodic function. Clearly, any technique designed to convert an analog filter into a digital one must take such factors into account.

To summarise, we need to be able to convert a transfer function $H(s)$ into a transfer function $H(z)$, so that the frequency response of the digital filter over the range $0 \leqslant \Omega \leqslant \pi$ approximates, in an acceptable manner, that of the analog filter over the range $0 \leqslant \omega \leqslant \infty$.

2.2.2 *The bilinear transformation*

One of the most effective and widely used techniques for converting an analog filter into a digital equivalent is by means of a bilinear transformation. The method can, in principle, be applied to a wide range of analog filter types. In practice it is perhaps most commonly applied to *Butterworth* and *Chebyshev* filters, which are among the best known of all analog filter families.

Butterworth and Chebyshev filters offer two different ways of approximating an ideal rectangular, or 'brickwall', response. This is illustrated for an analog low-pass filter in figure 2.16. A Butterworth approximation has a so-called *maximally-flat* passband characteristic: the gain falls off gradually towards the passband edge, passing through the -3 dB point at the nominal cut-off frequency ω_1. As the order (and hence complexity) of the

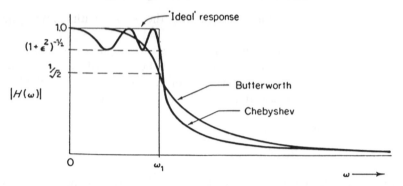

Figure 2.16   Typical frequency response (magnitude) functions of Butterworth and Chebyshev analog low-pass filters

filter is increased, its passband and stopband performances improve, and
the transition from passband to stopband becomes sharper.

The Chebyshev approximation gives an *equiripple* performance in the
passband. The response oscillates between 1.0 and $(1 + \epsilon^2)^{-1/2}$, where ϵ is
a ripple parameter controlled by the designer. The number of passband
ripples increases with the filter order; and the greater the ripple, the better
the stopband performance becomes. For a given order, stopband performance is superior to the Butterworth design, with a sharper transition.
Therefore a Chebyshev filter is generally preferred when some passband
ripple is acceptable.

The magnitude functions of these two important filter families are given
by

$$|H(\omega)| = \frac{1}{\left\{1 + \left(\dfrac{\omega}{\omega_1}\right)^{2n}\right\}^{1/2}} \quad \text{(Butterworth)} \tag{2.24}$$

and

$$|H(\omega)| = \frac{1}{\left\{1 + \epsilon^2 C_n^2\left(\dfrac{\omega}{\omega_1}\right)\right\}^{1/2}} \quad \text{(Chebyshev)} \tag{2.25}$$

where n is the filter order and ω_1 is the nominal cut-off frequency. C_n is the
Chebyshev polynomial of nth order. The amount of passband ripple δ is
related to the parameter ϵ by

$$\delta = 1 - (1 + \epsilon^2)^{-1/2} \tag{2.26}$$

The zero-order and first-order Chebyshev polynomials are

$$C_0(x) = 1 \quad \text{and} \quad C_1(x) = x \tag{2.27}$$

Second- and higher-order polynomials may be successively generated using the recursive relationship:

$$C_n(x) = 2x\, C_{n-1}(x) - C_{n-2}(x) \tag{2.28}$$

It is possible to derive equivalent high-pass and bandpass filters from a low-pass prototype. The techniques are part of the stock-in-trade of the analog filter designer. We shall see later that such flexibility is also possible in the case of digital filters.

Although the magnitude characteristics of Butterworth and Chebyshev filters are good, their phase characteristics depart considerably from ideal linear-phase, especially towards the cut-off point. In this respect they are inferior to the non-recursive designs covered previously.

The bilinear transformation may be introduced by considering the function:

$$F(z) = \frac{z - 1}{z + 1} \tag{2.29}$$

To explain its value in the present context we need to find its spectrum. Thus:

$$F(\Omega) = \frac{\exp(j\Omega) - 1}{\exp(j\Omega) + 1} = j \tan\left(\frac{\Omega}{2}\right) \tag{2.30}$$

$F(\Omega)$ is purely imaginary, and periodic. Its magnitude varies between 0 and ∞ as Ω varies between 0 and π.

Next, suppose we know the transfer function of a 'desirable' analog filter, expressed in the general form given by equation (2.23). Its frequency response is found by substituting $j\omega$ for s. Thus

$$H(\omega) = \frac{K(j\omega - z_1)(j\omega - z_2)(j\omega - z_3) \ldots}{(j\omega - p_1)(j\omega - p_2)(j\omega - p_3) \ldots} \tag{2.31}$$

The complete response is clearly generated as ω varies from 0 to ∞. If we now substitute $F(\Omega) = j \tan(\Omega/2)$ for $j\omega$, exactly the same values must be produced as Ω varies between 0 and π. Thus we obtain a function $H(\Omega)$ in which the complete frequency response of the analog filter is compressed into the range $0 \leqslant \Omega \leqslant \pi$. Note that the compression of the frequency scale is non-linear. The shape of the tan function means that the 'warping' effect is small near $\Omega = 0$, but increases greatly towards $\Omega = \pi$. Actually, as DSP designers we do not need to concern ourselves unduly with this effect. Butterworth and Chebyshev filters designed by this method are valid designs in their own right, and we can define their properties without continually referring back to the analog prototypes.

We may derive the transfer function $H(z)$ of such a filter by substituting $F(z)$ for s in equation (2.23). Fortunately, in the case of filters such as the Butterworth and Chebyshev families, the work has already been done, and we can use known formulae to specify $H(z)$, or the z-plane poles and zeros, directly. In the case of low-pass filters, the resulting magnitude responses are the same as those given in equations (2.24) and (2.25), but with Ω replaced by $\tan(\Omega/2)$. Thus

$$|H(\Omega)| = \frac{1}{\left\{1 + \left[\dfrac{\tan\Omega/2}{\tan\Omega_1/2}\right]^{2n}\right\}^{1/2}} \quad \text{(Butterworth)} \qquad (2.32)$$

and

$$|H(\Omega)| = \frac{1}{\left\{1 + \epsilon^2 C_n^2\left[\dfrac{\tan\Omega/2}{\tan\Omega_1/2}\right]\right\}^{1/2}} \quad \text{(Chebyshev)} \qquad (2.33)$$

There are several advantages in using the bilinear transformation for Butterworth and Chebyshev filters. Firstly, the 'maximally flat', or 'equi-ripple', amplitude properties of the filters are preserved when the frequency axis is compressed. Secondly, there is no aliasing of the original analog frequency response. Thus the response of a low-pass filter falls to zero at $\Omega = \pi$. This is a useful feature in many practical applications. Also, the method yields recursive filters which are computationally efficient.

Formulae for the z-plane pole and zero locations of such filters are given in various books and references on digital filters (see, for example, reference 4 in the Bibliography at the end of this book). We use such formulae in Computer Program 4 listed in appendix A, which calculates the poles and zeros of any Butterworth or Chebyshev filter with low-pass, high-pass, or bandpass characteristics. Then, knowing the poles and zeros, we can use Computer Program 5 to produce a decibel plot of the corresponding frequency response characteristic.

Let us illustrate with an example. Suppose we require a digital low-pass Butterworth filter having a cut-off frequency $\Omega_1 = 0.2\pi$, with a response at least '30 dB down' at $\Omega = 0.4\pi$. To find the required order of filter, we use equation (2.32) to give the response magnitude at $\Omega = 0.4\pi$. Thus

$$|H(0.4\pi)| = \cfrac{1}{\left\{1 + \left[\cfrac{\tan 0.2\pi}{\tan 0.1\pi}\right]^{2n}\right\}^{1/2}} = \frac{1}{(1 + 2.236^{2n})^{1/2}} \qquad (2.34)$$

Now -30 dB corresponds to a ratio of 0.03162. Hence we require that

$$\frac{1}{(1 + 2.236^{2n})^{1/2}} \leqslant 0.03162$$

giving

$$1 + 2.236^{2n} \geqslant 1000 \quad \text{or} \quad n \geqslant 4.29 \qquad (2.35)$$

Since the filter order must be an integer, we choose $n = 5$.

By running Computer Program 4, and selecting its Butterworth and low-pass options, we find that a fifth-order filter with a cut-off at $36°$ (0.2π) has a real zero, of order 5, at $z = -1$. Its pole locations, expressed in polar (r, θ) coordinates, are:

r	$\theta°$
0.50953	0
0.83221	34.644
0.59619	23.125

The first of these is interpreted as a first-order real pole at $z = 0.50953$. The others denote complex-conjugate pole pairs at r, $\pm \theta$. The filter's pole–zero configuration is sketched in part (a) of figure 2.17. The poles are seen to lie on a circular locus in the z-plane, which intersects the unit circle at points corresponding to the cut-off frequency.

Knowing the poles and zeros, we can find the difference equation of the filter. One approach is to multiply out the numerator and denominator polynomials of $H(z)$; however, this involves a lot of multiplication of coefficients (a problem which worsens as filter order increases). A convenient alternative is to treat the filter as a cascaded set of first- and

Digital Signals, Processors and Noise

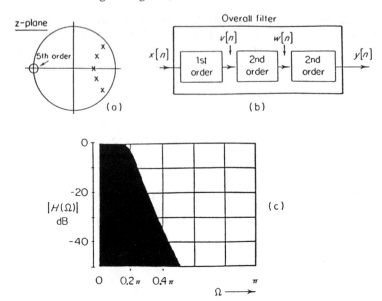

Figure 2.17   A fifth-order Butterworth low-pass digital filter (*abscissa of part (c): 320 samples*)

second-order subfilters, as shown in part (b) of the figure. The first-order subfilter has a single real pole and zero; each second-order subfilter comprises a complex pole-pair and a second-order zero. Note that intermediate outputs are labelled $v[n]$ and $w[n]$.

The transfer function of the first-order subfilter takes the form

$$\frac{V(z)}{X(z)} = \frac{(z + 1)}{(z - \alpha)} \tag{2.36}$$

giving the difference equation

$$v[n] = \alpha v[n - 1] + x[n] + x[n - 1] \tag{2.37}$$

Each second-order subfilter has a transfer function of the form

$$\frac{W(z)}{V(z)} = \frac{(z + 1)^2}{\{z - r \exp(j\theta)\}\{z - r \exp(-j\theta)\}}$$

$$= \frac{z^2 + 2z + 1}{z^2 - 2r \cos\theta\, z + r^2} \tag{2.38}$$

yielding a difference equation

$$w[n] = 2r\cos\theta\, w[n-1] - r^2\, w[n-2] + x[n] + 2x[n-1]$$
$$+ x[n-2] \tag{2.39}$$

Inserting the above pole values we readily obtain the following set of difference equations:

$$v[n] = 0.50953v[n-1] + x[n] + x[n-1]\}$$

$$w[n] = 1.3693w[n-1] - 0.69257w[n-2] + v[n] + 2v[n-1]$$
$$+ v[n-2]$$

$$y[n] = 1.0966y[n-1] - 0.35544y[n-2] + w[n] + 2w[n-1]$$
$$+ w[n-2] \tag{2.40}$$

The three equations are used together, the output of one feeding the input of the next. As already noted, an alternative would be to derive a single high-order difference equation involving just x and y.

We may also obtain a screen plot of the filter's frequency response using Computer Program 5 in appendix A. The program is fed with the following data:

No. of separate real poles:	1
value, order, of pole:	0.50953, 1
No. of separate real zeros:	1
value, order, of zero:	−1, 5
No. of complex pole pairs:	2
radius, angle, of each:	0.83221, 34.644
	0.59619, 23.125
No. of complex zero-pairs:	0

The program produces the screen plot shown in part (c) of figure 2.17. Note that the −3 dB point occurs at $\Omega = 0.2\pi$, and that the response is more than 30 dB down at $\Omega = 0.4\pi$, as required.

The program also prints out the maximum gain of the filter. In this case it occurs at $\Omega = 0$, and equals 780 (57.8 dB). If this scaling effect is unacceptable, it can be offset by multiplying all input sample values by 1/780; or by sharing the factor between the three difference equations.

If we can accept some passband ripple, a Chebyshev design should allow us to meet the same stopband specification with a filter of lower order. For example, if we allow a 3 dB passband ripple (equivalent to a fractional ripple of 0.2929), and use Computer Programs 4 and 5 as before, it turns out that a third-order Chebyshev filter meets the above specification – and involves considerably less computation. The resulting frequency response plot is shown in part (a) of figure 2.18.

Computer Program 4 may also be used to design high-pass and bandpass filters. Referring back to part (a) of figure 2.17, we see that a low-pass filter's poles are clustered around $z= 1$, with a high-order zero at $z = -1$. An equivalent high-pass design is readily obtained by changing the sign of the real parts of all poles and zeros, giving a 'mirror-image' pole–zero pattern. The frequency response plot of a sixth-order Butterworth high-pass filter designed in this way is shown in part (b) of figure 2.18.

To find the poles and zeros of a bandpass filter, Computer Program 4 uses a *low-pass to bandpass transformation*. The resulting bandpass filter has twice as many poles and zeros as the low-pass prototype, so its order is always even. The pole–zero configuration and frequency response plot of a tenth-order Chebyshev bandpass filter with 2 dB passband ripple are shown in figure 2.19.

We hope you will have the opportunity to use Computer Programs 4 and 5 to investigate further examples of Butterworth and Chebyshev filters – bearing in mind that they are not the only types of digital filter which can be successfully designed using the bilinear transformation!

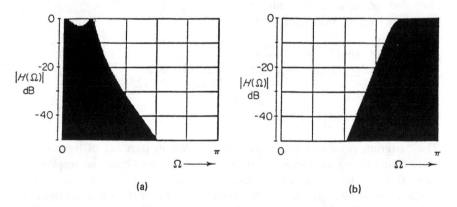

Figure 2.18   Frequency responses of (a) a third-order Chebyshev low-pass filter, and (b) a sixth-order Butterworth high-pass filter (*abscissa: 320 samples*)

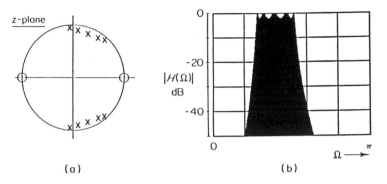

Figure 2.19 A tenth-order Chebyshev bandpass filter (*abscissa: 320 samples*)

2.2.3 *Impulse-invariant filters*

Another method of deriving a digital filter from an analog filter is known as impulse-invariance. In this case the design criterion is that the impulse response of the digital filter should be a sampled version of that of the analog reference filter. It produces a different relationship between the analog and digital filters in the frequency domain, compared with the bilinear transformation. In practice impulse-invariance tends to be less effective, and rather more awkward to use. Nevertheless the technique involves some important ideas, which are valuable for illustrating the links between analog and digital LTI processors.

Figure 2.20 illustrates impulse-invariance in the time and frequency domains. Part (a) shows the impulse response $h(t)$ and frequency response magnitude $|H(\omega)|$ of the reference analog filter. We have chosen a low-pass characteristic – although there is no special significance in the form of the curves. Part (b) of the figure shows the impulse response $h[n]$ of an impulse-invariant digital filter, which is simply equal to a sampled version of $h(t)$ with sampling interval T. Thus

$$h_1[n] = h(nT_1), \quad n = 0, 1, 2 \ldots \tag{2.41}$$

In section 1.2 we saw how sampling a continuous-time function causes repetition of its spectrum at multiples of the sampling frequency. We therefore expect that the frequency response of our impulse-invariant filter will be a repeating version of that of the analog filter. It follows that if we sample at too low a rate, there will be significant spectral overlap, leading to aliasing. The digital filter's frequency response will then be a poor replica of the characteristic we are trying to copy.

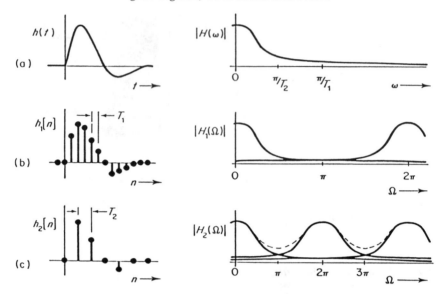

Figure 2.20   Impulse-invariance in the time and frequency domains

It is important to note that, in general, the frequency response of an analog low-pass filter only tends to zero as $\omega \to \infty$. It follows that a certain amount of aliasing is inherent in the impulse-invariant approach. However, this can be made small by ensuring that the samples of $h(t)$ are closely spaced – as in part (b) of the figure.

Part (c) of the figure shows the effects of reducing the sampling rate to half its previous value, defining an alternative impulse-invariant filter. The aliasing effect is now much more serious. We conclude that the effectiveness of the technique depends on choosing an adequate sampling rate, and an analog reference filter with a limited bandwidth.

There are two further potential difficulties. First, the sampled impulse response, as it stands, gives the coefficients for a non-recursive filter. This may be very uneconomic. Second, most books and references on analog filters specify transfer functions rather than impulse responses. We therefore need to develop a frequency domain approach – and one which will provide us with an economic, recursive algorithm.

The best way forward is as follows. First, we look up the transfer function of the reference analog filter, which is likely to be given in the series form of equation (2.23). Assuming there are no repeated poles (that is, no poles of second or higher order), we may use a partial fraction expansion to recast $H(s)$ in the following parallel form:

$$H(s) = \frac{K_1}{(s - p_1)} + \frac{K_2}{(s - p_2)} + \frac{K_3}{(s - p_3)} + \ldots \tag{2.42}$$

In effect we are decomposing the analog filter into a set of single-pole subfilters, whose outputs are added together. This is illustrated by part (a) of figure 2.21.

It is quite straightforward to specify a digital, impulse-invariant version of each subfilter. This is because the impulse response of each analog subfilter takes a simple exponential form. Thus, for the ith subfilter:

$$h_i(t) = K_i \exp(p_i t), \quad t \geq 0$$

$$= 0, \qquad\qquad t < 0 \tag{2.43}$$

The impulse response of the impulse-invariant digital subfilter is therefore

$$h_i[n] = h_i(nT) \tag{2.44}$$

where T is the chosen sampling interval. Using equation (2.43) we have

$$h_i[n] = K_i \exp(np_i T) \quad n \geq 0$$

$$= 0, \qquad\qquad n < 0 \tag{2.45}$$

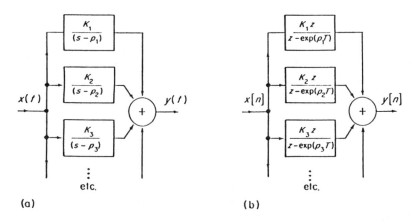

(a)   (b)

Figure 2.21   Designing an impulse-invariant filter by parallel decomposition

The transfer function of the digital subfilter equals the z-Transform of its impulse response. Fortunately this is easily found:

$$H_i[z] = \sum_{n=0}^{\infty} K_i \exp(np_iT)\, z^{-n} = \sum_{n=0}^{\infty} K_i \{\exp(p_iT)\, z^{-1}\}^n$$

$$= \frac{K_i}{1 - \exp(p_iT)z^{-1}} = \frac{K_iz}{z - \exp(p_iT)} \tag{2.46}$$

The complete digital filter is now built up as a parallel set of subfilters, as shown in part (b) of figure 2.21. Like the analog case, the overall impulse response is simply equal to the sum of the individual impulse responses. And since each of these is impulse-invariant, so is the complete filter.

Equation (2.46) shows that each digital subfilter has a zero at the origin of the z-plane, and a pole at $z = \exp(p_iT)$. Actually the zero is not essential, because it does not affect the shape of the frequency response. However it does ensure that the subfilter is minimum-delay.

Let us now apply the above ideas to a practical design, and compare it with a similar filter based upon the bilinear transformation. We will take a third-order Butterworth low-pass filter with a cut-off frequency of 1 radian/second as our starting point. Its transfer function, widely tabulated in the analog filter literature, is

$$H(s) = \frac{1}{(s + 1)(s + 0.5 + j0.866)(s + 0.5 - j0.866)} \tag{2.47}$$

We will choose a sampling interval $T = 0.5$ s. The first task is to use a partial fraction expansion to express $H(s)$ in parallel form. This involves some rather awkward algebra, but is otherwise straightforward. We then use equation (2.46) to establish the component parts of the digital transfer function, and obtain

$$H(z) = \frac{z}{(z - 0.6065)} + \frac{z(0.8956 - z)}{(z^2 - 1.414z + 0.6065)} \tag{2.48}$$

The filter can either be implemented in this form, as paralleled first- and second-order subsystems; or we can convert into the series form. The latter is helpful here because it allows us to use Computer Program 5 in appendix A (which assumes the series form) to obtain a screen plot of the frequency response. After some further algebra we obtain

$$H(z) = \frac{0.08701z(z + 0.7315)}{(z^3 - 2.0203z^2 + 1.464z - 0.3678)} \tag{2.49}$$

The filter's difference equation is therefore

$$y[n] = 2.0203y[n - 1] - 1.464y[n - 2] + 0.3678y[n - 3]$$
$$+ 0.08701x[n - 1] + 0.06365x[n - 2] \tag{2.50}$$

$H(z)$ has poles at $z = 0.6065$, and at $z = r \exp(\pm j\theta)$ where $r = 0.7788$ and $\theta = 0.433$ radian (24.8°). It has zeros at $z = 0$ and at $z = -0.7315$. Using this data as input to Computer Program 5 produces the screen plot in part (a) of figure 2.22. In this case $\Omega = \pi$ corresponds to $\omega = \pi/T = 6.28$ radians/second. We see that the −3 dB cut-off point occurs at $\omega = 1$, as required.

Part (b) of the figure shows the frequency response plot for a third-order Butterworth filter designed by the bilinear transformation method. The cut-off frequency is $\Omega = \omega T = 0.5$ radian, or 28.65°. Note that the two plots are very similar at low frequencies. However the cut-off slope of the impulse-invariant filter is less steep at higher frequencies, because of some aliasing of the analog characteristic. This disadvantage is partly offset by the fact that the impulse-invariant filter has fewer z-plane zeros and requires slightly less computation.

The poles and zeros of the impulse-invariant filter are sketched in part (a) of figure 2.23. Only one of the zeros contributes to shaping the frequency response characteristic, compared with three zeros in the equivalent bilinear transformation design.

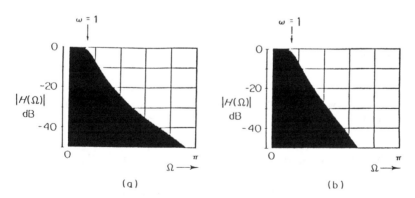

Figure 2.22 Responses of third-order Butterworth low-pass filters designed by (a) impulse invariance, and (b) the bilinear transformation (*abscissa: 320 samples*)

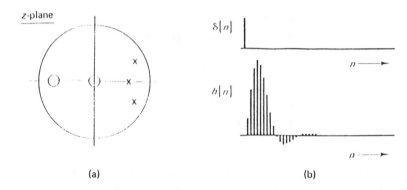

Figure 2.23   (a) Pole–zero configuration, and (b) impulse response of an
impulse-invariant Butterworth low-pass filter (*abscissa: 50
samples*)

Part (b) of figure 2.23 shows a unit impulse and, below it, the computed
impulse response of the filter. This must be a sampled version (with
$T = 0.5$ s) of the impulse response of the reference analog filter.

You may well feel that impulse-invariant design is rather awkward,
involving some cumbersome algebra. Not surprisingly, most serious users
of the technique rely on substantial help from a digital computer! Although
our approach here has been strictly introductory, we hope that it has given
a good idea of the basis of the method, and illustrated some important
relationships between analog and digital processors.

Problems

Section 2.1

2.1. Predict the form of the frequency response of the following low-pass
moving average filters, and sketch their z-plane pole–zero configurations:

(a) 9-term impulse response, all terms equal to 1/9
(b) 19-term impulse response, all terms equal to 1/19.

2.2. Use the inverse Fourier Transform to find the impulse response $h[n]$
of:

(a) An ideal, zero-phase, low-pass filter with cut-off frequency
$\Omega_1 = 0.4\pi$. The filter should have unity gain in the passband and
zero gain in the stopband.

(b) An ideal high-pass filter with cut-off frequency $\Omega_1 = 0.8\pi$. Its characteristics are otherwise like those in part (a).

In each case, sketch the impulse response of a causal, linear-phase version of the filter with its impulse response truncated to fifteen terms.

2.3. Tabulate the sample values of:

(a) a von Hann window with 11 terms
(b) a Hamming window with 13 terms.

You need only estimate 'one half' of each window.

2.4. The simplest LTI processor which can be used to give an approximate differentiation of a digital signal computes the *first-order difference*:

$$y[n] = x[n] - x[n-1]$$

A less-widely used alternative is to estimate the *central difference*, using the algorithm:

$$y[n] = 0.5x[n] - 0.5x[n-2]$$

Sketch the magnitude responses of the two approximations on the same diagram, over the range $0 \leqslant \Omega \leqslant \pi$. Contrast their performance with that of an ideal differentiator. By how many dB is each response lower than that of an ideal differentiator at the frequency 0.2π?

Section 2.2

2.5. Sketch, to linear scales, the frequency response (magnitude) of recursive filters specified by the following z-plane pole–zero locations:

(a) pole at $z = -0.9$, zero at $z = 1$
(b) poles at $z = \pm j0.95$, zeros at $z = \pm 1$
(c) second-order pole at $z = 0.95$, zeros at $z = -0.5 \pm j0.8$.

2.6. Design a simple digital bandstop ('notch') filter with the following characteristics:

(a) sampling rate 1000 Hz
(b) rejection of signal components in the range 100 Hz $\pm$ 10 Hz (to -3 dB points)
(c) approximately unity gain in the passband.

Sketch the pole–zero configuration, and specify the difference equation.

2.7. Make an accurate sketch of the frequency response (in dB) of a third-order Butterworth digital low-pass filter based on the bilinear transformation, with cut-off frequency $\Omega_1 = 0.2\,\pi$.

2.8. Using Computer Program 4 in appendix A, find and sketch the z-plane poles and zeros of the following digital filters, based on the bilinear transformation:
(a) Butterworth low-pass, seventh-order, cut-off frequency $\Omega_1 = 0.3\,\pi$
(b) Chebyshev low-pass, sixth-order, 20 per cent ripple, cut-off frequency $\Omega_1 = 0.4\,\pi$
(c) Butterworth high-pass, fourth-order, cut-off frequency $0.8\,\pi$
(d) Chebyshev bandpass, eighth-order, 3 dB ripple, passband edges at 0.2π and 0.5π.

2.9. You are asked to design a Butterworth digital high-pass flter with a cut-off frequency $= 0.7\pi$. Its response should be at least 30 dB down at 0.5π, and at least 50 db down at 0.3π. What minimum order of filter is required?

2.10. Using Computer Program 4 in appendix A, find the poles and zeros of a Chebyshev third-order high-pass filter with cut-off frequency $\Omega_1 = 0.9\pi$ and 3 dB passband ripple. Then use Computer Program 5 to plot the filter's frequency response. What cut-off (in dB) does the filter achieve at $\Omega = 0.8\pi$?

Specify the filter's difference equation, corrected to give a peak gain of unity in the passband.

2.11. An analog bandpass filter has the transfer function

$$H(s) = \frac{s}{(s + 1)(s + 2)}$$

where s is the Laplace variable. Design a recursive impulse-invariant filter based on a sampling interval of $0.1s$, giving your answer in terms of a single difference equation relating input and output.

Use Computer Program 5 in appendix A to plot the frequency response of the filter, checking that it has a bandpass characteristic. (*Note*: the program does not require the details of any poles or zeros at the *origin*, because they have no effect on the response magnitude function.)

2.12. A Butterworth analog low-pass filter of fourth order, with cut-off frequency of 1 radian/second, has the transfer function

$$H(s) = \frac{1}{(s^2 + 1.8478s + 1)(s^2 + 0.7654s + 1)}$$

Design a recursive, impulse-invariant, digital filter based on a sampling interval of $0.25s$. Specify difference equations for a parallel form realisation.

2.13. Recast the difference equations found in problem **2.12** as a single equation representing a series form realisation of the filter. Hence use Computer Program 5 in appendix A to plot its frequency response.

3 The Discrete and Fast Fourier Transforms

The Discrete Fourier Transform (DFT) is of central importance in Digital Signal Processing. When implemented using a Fast Fourier Transform (FFT) algorithm, it offers rapid frequency-domain analysis and processing of digital signals, and investigation of digital systems. The development of FFT algorithms from the mid-1960s onwards gave a huge impetus to DSP, making practicable a range of valuable techniques.

Back in section 1.4 we described two Fourier representations for digital signals: a discrete-time version of the classical Fourier Series, applicable to strictly periodic signals; and a discrete-time version of the Fourier Transform, applicable to aperiodic signals and LTI processors. The DFT may be regarded as a third Fourier representation, relevant to digital signals of finite length. It is closely related to the earlier material – especially to that on the Fourier Series – and you may therefore find it helpful to review section 1.4 before proceeding.

3.1 The Discrete Fourier Transform (DFT)

We rarely encounter a truly periodic signal in practical DSP. Far more common are aperiodic signals and data having a finite number of sample values – for example, the stock market data of figure 1.1, or the EMG of figure 1.3. The DFT of such a signal $x[n]$, defined for $0 \leqslant n \leqslant (N - 1)$, is given by

$$X(k) = \sum_{n=0}^{N-1} x[n] \exp(-j2\pi \, kn/N) = \sum_{n=0}^{N-1} x[n] \, W_N^{kn} \qquad (3.1)$$

where $W_N = \exp(-j2\pi/N)$ and the spectral coefficients $X[k]$ are evaluated for $0 \leqslant k \leqslant (N - 1)$. The inverse DFT, or IDFT, which allows us to recover the signal from its spectrum, is given by

$$x[n] = \frac{1}{N} \sum_{k=0}^{N-1} X[k] \, W_N^{-kn} \tag{3.2}$$

where the values of $x[n]$ are evaluated for $0 \leq n \leq (N-1)$.

If we use equation (3.1) to compute additional values of $X[k]$, outside the range $0 \leq k \leq (N-1)$, we find that they form a periodic spectral sequence. Likewise, using equation (3.2) to calculate additional values of $x[n]$, outside the range $0 \leq n \leq (N-1)$, yields a periodic version of the signal. We therefore see that the DFT and IDFT both represent a finite-length sequence as one period of a periodic sequence. In effect the DFT considers a practical, aperiodic, signal to be periodic for the purposes of computation.

Note that equations (3.1) and (3.2) are essentially similar to the analysis and synthesis equations of the Discrete Fourier Series, (equations (1.21) and (1.22)). The only difference is that we have now incorporated the scaling factor $1/N$ in the synthesis equation (in line with the usual definition of the DFT), and have denoted the spectral coefficients by $X[k]$ in order to emphasise the transform–pair relationship between a signal and its spectrum.

This similarity suggests that equation (3.1) may be viewed in two ways. If the signal $x[n]$ is truly periodic, the equation yields a Discrete Fourier series; but if $x[n]$ is basically aperiodic, and only being treated as periodic for the purposes of computation, then the equation represents the DFT. However there is no need to get concerned about this; a periodic signal with period N, and an aperiodic signal of length N, are both completely defined by N sample values!

Why do we use the DFT for aperiodic signals, rather than the discrete-time version of the Fourier Transform described in section 1.4? The basic reason has to do with computation. The Fourier Transform $X[\Omega]$ of an aperiodic signal is a continuous function of the variable Ω. But a digital computer cannot work with a continuous function; all it can do is estimate values of the function for a discrete set of Ω values – in other words, compute a set of *frequency-domain samples*. This is exactly what the DFT does; furthermore, it produces just enough samples to define the signal completely in the frequency domain.

The key to understanding this important idea is provided by a frequency-domain version of the famous Sampling Theorem first discussed in section 1.2. It may be stated as follows;

The continuous spectrum of a signal of limited duration T_0 seconds may be completely represented by regularly-spaced frequency-domain samples spaced not more than $1/T_0$ Hz apart.

Now an aperiodic digital signal with N sample values has a duration $T_0 = NT$ seconds, where T is the sampling interval in the time domain. Hence its spectrum can be completely represented by frequency-domain samples spaced $1/NT$ Hz, or $2\pi/NT$ radians per second, apart. Since the variable Ω equals ωT, where ω is the radian frequency, it follows that we must sample at intervals in Ω of $2\pi/N$ (or less).

Remember that the spectrum of a digital signal (or the frequency response of a digital processor) is always periodic in Ω, with period 2π. Since one period is clearly sufficient to define it, sampling at the minimum interval of $2\pi/N$ gives us $2\pi \div 2\pi/N = N$ frequency-domain samples.

Returning to equations (3.1) and (3.2), we see that the DFT does just this. It provides N distinct spectral coefficients for a signal with N distinct sample values; conversely, the IDFT regenerates the N signal values from the N spectral coefficients. The values of $X[k]$ are effectively samples of the 'underlying' Fourier Transform $X(\Omega)$. And the DFT, by just obeying the Sampling Theorem in the frequency domain, gives us the most economic spectral representation possible.

The DFT copes with complex, as well as real, signals. If a signal has N complex sample values (each with a real and imaginary part) then it has $2N$ degrees of freedom in the time domain. The N values of its spectrum are also complex, giving $2N$ degrees of freedom in the frequency domain. Conversely, a real signal has just N degrees of freedom in the time domain. In this case it turns out that half the spectral coefficients are sufficient to define the spectrum, because the other half displays a 'mirror-image' pattern – a point already made in section 1.4. Thus whether the signal is real or complex, the DFT gives the same number of degrees of freedom in the two domains. This attractive result stems from the symmetry of Fourier Transformation.

The relationships between the DFT, the Fourier Transform, and the Discrete Fourier Series are summarised by figure 3.1. Part (a) shows a real aperiodic signal $x[n]$ and, on the right-hand side, its spectrum (only the magnitude is given, for convenience). The spectrum is continuous and periodic. Since we are here assuming a real-time function, the portion between 0 and π is a mirror-image of that between π and 2π. This means that the spectrum may be completely defined by its fluctuations over any frequency interval equal to π. Part (b) of the figure shows a periodic version of the same signal, and, on the right, its Discrete Fourier Series (which is also periodic). The spectral coefficients may be regarded as samples of $X(\Omega)$. Finally, the figure shows that the DFT estimates a single period of the repetitive spectrum, and the IDFT a single period of the repetitive signal – as indicated by the dotted lines.

Not surprisingly, the DFT has a number of important properties, which parallel those of the Discrete Fourier Series (see table B.1). They include *linearity*, *time-shifting*, *convolution* and *modulation*, and we include them

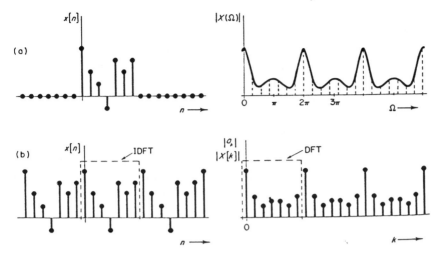

Figure 3.1 Relationships between the DFT, Fourier Transform and discrete Fourier series

as table B.5 in appendix B. One important point to note is that in the case of the DFT all time shifts are evaluated *modulo-N*; this is because of the essentially periodic, or *circular*, nature of the DFT and IDFT. The matter is covered more fully in several of the books listed in the Bibliography at the end of the book, and we shall have more to say about it later in this chapter.

We next make some comments about the problem of computing the DFT. Probably the major one, from a practical point of view, is speed. It is a complicated question, which depends not only on the precise algorithm and programming language used, but also on the hardware. In many cases the multiplications demanded by the DFT or IDFT are the most time-consuming operations (unless the hardware has been specifically designed to achieve fast multiplication); so it is worth considering just how many of them are required.

It turns out that some $4N^2$ floating-point multiplications are needed to implement equations (3.1) and (3.2) directly for a complex signal; this reduces to about $2N^2$ if the signal is real. In either case there is a similar number of integer multiplications and floating-point additions/subtractions to be performed. In general, we may expect the computation time to be roughly proportional to N^2. If you have run even a short DFT program (say for $N = 64$ or 128) on a personal computer, you will know that it may take a minute or so to execute. This implies that a 2048-point signal could take several hours! Of course these times reduce with a more powerful machine – but even so they are likely to be serious.

In addition to the problem of multiplication, implementation of the DFT and IDFT equations as they stand requires a lot of trigonometric (sine and cosine) evaluations. These can effectively be reduced by using a *table look-up*, in which the required values are calculated just once, and stored. Other modifications and improvements may also be possible. For example, some of the values of a signal may be zero, and can be omitted from the computation. Sometimes all N values of the spectrum are not needed. If the cost of test and branch instructions in a program is high, it may be better to incorporate portions of *straight-line code*. But even when all this has been done, careful inspection of the DFT and IDFT equations reveals that they still involve a lot of redundant calculation. It is this, above all, which Fast Fourier Transform (FFT) algorithms attempt to eliminate.

3.2 The Fast Fourier Transform (FFT)

3.2.1 Basis of the FFT

A series of highly efficient algorithms for computing the DFT were first developed in the 1960s. Collectively known as Fast Fourier Transforms (FFTs), they rely on the fact that the standard DFT involves redundant calculation. Referring back to equation (3.1), it turns out that the same values of $x[n]W_N^{kn}$ are calculated many times as the computation proceeds – particularly if the transform is lengthy. This is because W_N^{kn} is a periodic function with a limited number of distinct values. It is the aim of FFTs to eliminate such redundancy.

Strictly speaking there is no such thing as 'the FFT'. Rather there is a collection of algorithms with different features, advantages and limitations. An algorithm suitable for programming in a high-level language on a general-purpose computer may not be suitable for special-purpose DSP hardware. What all the algorithms have in common, however, is their general approach – *decomposition* of the DFT into a number of successively shorter, simpler DFTs.

In this section we will start by showing how a DFT can be expressed in terms of such shorter DFTs, using what we will call *conventional decomposition*. This approach is widely adopted in the DSP literature. We will then go on to develop various types of FFT algorithm using an alternative technique known as *index mapping*, which offers a particularly compact and convenient notation, and may readily be applied to DFTs of any length which is not prime (even though we restrict ourselves here to transform lengths equal to an integer power of 2). It is important to realise that conventional decomposition and index mapping are two ways of looking at the same problem; there is no essential difference between them.

Conventional decomposition may be introduced by breaking a signal $x[n]$ down into two shorter, interleaved subsequences. The process, known as *decimation-in-time*, produces one of the major classes of FFT algorithm. Suppose we have a signal with N sample values, where N is an integer power of 2. We first separate $x[n]$ into two subsequences, each with $N/2$ samples. One subsequence contains the even-numbered points in $x[n]$; the other contains the odd-numbered points. Writing $n = 2r$, when n is even, and $n = 2r + 1$ when n is odd, the DFT is recast as:

$$X(k) = \sum_{n=0}^{N-1} x[n] \, W_N^{kn}, \quad 0 \le k \le (N-1)$$

$$= \sum_{r=0}^{N/2-1} x[2r] \, W_N^{2rk} + \sum_{r=0}^{N/2-1} x[2r+1] \, W_N^{(2r+1)k}$$

$$= \sum_{r=0}^{N/2-1} x[2r] \, (W_N^2)^{rk} + W_N^k \sum_{r=0}^{N/2-1} x[2r+1] \, (W_N^2)^{rk} \qquad (3.3)$$

Now since

$$W_N^2 = \exp(-2\mathrm{j}2\pi/N) = W_{N/2} \qquad (3.4)$$

we may write

$$X[k] = \sum_{r=0}^{N/2-1} x[2r] \, W_{N/2}^{rk} + W_N^k \sum_{r=0}^{N/2-1} x[2r+1] \, W_{N/2}^{rk}$$

$$= G[k] + W_N^k \, H[k] \qquad (3.5)$$

The original N-point DFT has now been expressed in terms of two $N/2$-point DFTs, $G[k]$ and $H[k]$. $G[k]$ is the transform of the even-numbered points in $x[n]$, and $H[k]$ is the transform of the odd-numbered points. Note that (unfortunately!) we must multiply $H[k]$ by an additional term W_N^k before adding it to $G[k]$. This is because the subsequences into which we have decomposed $x[n]$ are displaced from one another in time by one sampling interval. If you refer to table B.5 in appendix B, you will see that such a time shift is indeed equivalent to multiplying the corresponding spectrum by W_N^k.

If the transform length N is an integer power of 2, it follows that $N/2$ is even. Therefore we can take the decomposition further by breaking each $N/2$-point subsequence down into two shorter, $N/4$-point, subsequences. The process can continue until, in the limit, we are left with a series of 2-point subsequences, each of which requires a very simple 2-point DFT. A complete decomposition of this type gives rise to one of the commonly-used *radix-2*, *decimation-in-time*, FFT algorithms.

However, we must not assume that the resulting computation is trivial. Although each 2-point DFT involves very simple arithmetic, we have already seen that the transform of a sequence cannot be found by merely adding the transforms of its subsequences. This is because the subsequences are displaced from each other in time-origin. As we decompose a lengthy DFT into successively shorter DFTs, these time displacements arise at every stage of the decomposition. Furthermore (just to be awkward!) they are different at each stage, because the time shifts and intervals between samples are different.

Part of the challenge in designing effective FFT algorithms lies in incorporating these unwelcome, but necessary, factors in such a way that the amount of computation is minimised. It is quite possible to develop the ideas further in terms of conventional decomposition (see, for example, the book by Oppenheim and Schafer listed as reference 5 in the Bibliography at the end of this book). However, for reasons noted earlier, we will ourselves use the alternative approach known as *index mapping*.

3.2.2 Index mapping

The technique of index mapping may be introduced by expressing the transform length N as the product of two factors N_1 and N_2:

$$N = N_1 N_2 \tag{3.6}$$

We also define two new indices n_1 and n_2:

$$n_1 = 0, 1, 2 \dots (N_1 - 1) \tag{3.7}$$

and

$$n_2 = 0, 1, 2 \dots (N_2 - 1) \tag{3.8}$$

The following linear equation may now be used to *map* the values of n_1 and n_2 into the time-index n of the DFT:

$$n = (M_1 n_1 + M_2 n_2)_N \tag{3.9}$$

where M_1 and M_2 are constants, and the brackets and subscript N denote modulo-N. The mapping is made one-to-one, in the sense that all the required values of n ($0 \leqslant n \leqslant N - 1$) are generated once, and once only, as n_1 and n_2 vary over their specified ranges. In a similar way, the frequency-index k of the DFT can be mapped using

$$k = (J_1 k_1 + J_2 k_2)_N \tag{3.10}$$

In general, it is the form of equations (3.9) and (3.10), and the choice of the various constants, which define a particular FFT decomposition.

We begin with a simple example: a 4-point DFT which we will decompose into 2-point DFTs. In this case $N = 4$ and $N_1 = N_2 = 2$. We choose $M_1 = 2$, $M_2 = 1$, $J_1 = 1$ and $J_2 = 2$. Hence

$$n = 2n_1 + n_2 \quad \text{and} \quad k = k_1 + 2k_2 \tag{3.11}$$

with n_1, n_2, k_1 and k_2 all taken over the range 0 to 1. The mappings of n and k are shown in figure 3.2. Note that each of the required values of n and k is represented once, and once only.

The DFT for $n = 4$ is given by

$$X(k) = \sum_{n=0}^{N-1} x[n] \, W_N^{kn} = \sum_{n=0}^{3} x[n] \, W_4^{kn} \tag{3.12}$$

It is helpful to substitute initially for n (but not for k) using equation (3.11). Also, writing $X[k]$ as X and $x[n]$ as x for simplicity, we obtain

$$X = \sum_{n_2=0}^{1} \sum_{n_1=0}^{1} x \, W_4^{2kn_1} \, W_4^{kn_2} \tag{3.13}$$

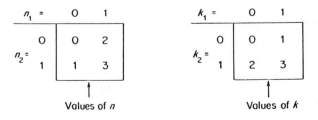

Figure 3.2   Index maps for a 4-point FFT decomposition

Since $W_4^{kn_2}$ is not a function of n_1, we have

$$X = \sum_{n_2=0}^{1} W_4^{kn_2} \sum_{n_1=0}^{1} x \, W_4^{2kn_1} \qquad (3.14)$$

giving

$$X = 1 \sum_{n_1=0}^{1} x \, W_4^{2kn_1} + W_4^{k} \sum_{n_1=0}^{1} x \, W_4^{2kn_1} \qquad (3.15)$$

It may be shown that index-mapping has achieved the same result as conventional decomposition, expressed by equation (3.5); indeed, equation (3.15) becomes the same as equation (3.5) if we put $N = 4$. This confirms that the index-mappings shown in figure 3.2 are equivalent to a decimation-in-time of the original 4-point sequence into two 2-point subsequences.

Evaluating the W_4 terms modulo-4, equation (3.15) gives the following complete set of equations for the 4-point transform:

$$X[0] = \{x[0] + x[2] \, W_4^{0}\} + W_4^{0}\{x[1] + x[3] \, W_4^{0}\}$$

$$X[1] = \{x[0] + x[2] \, W_4^{2}\} + W_4^{1}\{x[1] + x[3] \, W_4^{2}\}$$

$$X[2] = \{x[0] + x[2] \, W_4^{0}\} + W_4^{2}\{x[1] + x[3] \, W_4^{0}\}$$

$$X[3] = \{x[0] + x[2] \, W_4^{2}\} + W_4^{3}\{x[1] + x[3] \, W_4^{2}\} \qquad (3.16)$$

This way of representing a 4-point DFT may be visualised more easily with the help of the *signal flow graph* in figure 3.3. Starting on the left-hand side with the data values, we go through two stages of processing, ending up on the right-hand side with the DFT coefficients $X[0]$ to $X[3]$. Each stage of processing involves two 2-point DFTs, and the overall scheme defines a radix-2 FFT algorithm. Note that the convention used in the figure is that branches entering a node are summed to give the variable at that node. Weightings, or *transmittances*, are represented by circular symbols, with the number inside each symbol representing a power of W_4. By following paths through the graph we can express any of the outputs (X) in terms of the inputs (x). You may like to check equations (3.16) in this way.

The flow graph structure, and the branch transmittances, are directly related to our index-mapping equations (3.14) and (3.15). Thus the inner sum over n_1 in equation (3.14) gives the transmittance values in the first

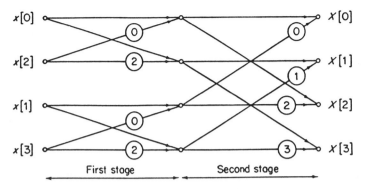

Figure 3.3 Signal flow graph for a 4-point, in-place decimation-in-time FFT algorithm with shuffled input and natural-order output. The branch transmittances are expressed as powers of W_4

processing stage; the outer sum over n_2 gives the transmittances in the second stage. Note how each node has two input and/or output branches; and how the vertical span of the individual 2-point DFTs increases as we move from left to right across the graph.

It is important to note that, whereas the output data is arranged in *natural order*, the input data has been *shuffled*. This is because the initial 2-point DFTs require $x[0]$ to be paired with $x[2]$, and $x[1]$ to be paired with $x[3]$. The correct input sequence can be deduced from the index maps of figure 3.2. Comparing values of n and k in the two 'boxes', we see that if the output index k is taken through the natural-order sequence 0–1–2–3, the corresponding locations in the 'n-box' give the shuffled sequence 0–2–1–3.

The transmittances in this 4-point FFT decomposition have the following simple arithmetic values:

$$W_4^0 = 1 \qquad\qquad W_4^1 = \exp(-j2\pi/4) = -j$$

$$W_4^2 = (W_4^1)^2 = j^2 = -1 \qquad W_4^3 = W_4^1 W_4^2 = j \qquad\qquad (3.17)$$

Hence the symbols '0' and '2' in figure 3.3 imply just addition/subtraction; symbols '1' and '3' denote weighting by j – in other words, conversions from real to imaginary. We see that a length-4 FFT is quite a simple affair, requiring a few elementary data manipulations – and no floating-point multiplications at all.

3.2.3 Twiddle factors and FFT butterflies

The FFT algorithm we have just developed reduces a 4-point DFT to a set of simpler 2-point DFTs. It should therefore be possible to express the branch transmittances shown in figure 3.3 as powers of W_2, rather than W_4. Now

$$W_2 = \exp(-j2\pi/2) = -1$$

and hence

$$W_4^0 = 1 = W_2^0; \quad W_4^2 = W_2^1 = -1; \quad W_4^3 = W_4^2 W_4^1 = W_2^1 W_4^1$$
$$(3.18)$$

Making these substitutions, we get the alternative signal flow graph in figure 3.4. Although most of the transmittances have indeed been recast as powers of W_2 (and therefore have values ± 1), we cannot eliminate the terms W_4^1. They are referred to as *twiddle factors*, and represent additional arithmetic over and above that required by the 'straight' 2-point transforms in the first stage of processing. Note that, in this example, the two twiddle factors could easily be combined, because they occur in branches coming from the same node – a point we return to a little later.

You may recall our earlier discussion of the additional multiplier W_N^k which arose when we decimated a signal into subsequences, and expressed its transform in terms of the transforms of the subsequences (equation (3.5)). Twiddle factors arise in the same way. They represent the additional computations needed, after the complete DFT has been recast (as far as possible) in terms of elementary 2-point transforms.

It is quite possible to derive the transmittances and twiddle factors of figure 3.4 by re-examining equation (3.14). Substituting for k as well as n (using equation (3.11)) we have:

$$X = \sum_{n_2=0}^{1} W_4^{(k_1+2k_2)n_2} \sum_{n_1=0}^{1} x \, W_4^{2(k_1+2k_2)n_1}$$

$$= \sum_{n_2=0}^{1} W_4^{k_1 n_2} W_4^{2k_2 n_2} \sum_{n_1=0}^{1} x \, W_4^{2k_1 n_1} W_4^{4k_2 n_1} \qquad (3.19)$$

Now $W_4^{4k_2 n_1} = W_4^0 = 1$ for all values of k_2 and n_1, so it does not contribute. Furthermore $W_4^2 = W_2$. Therefore

$$X = \sum_{n_2=0}^{1} W_4^{k_1 n_2} W_2^{k_2 n_2} \sum_{n_1=0}^{1} x \, W_2^{k_1 n_1} \qquad (3.20)$$

Comparing with figure 3.4 we see that the term $W_2^{k_1 n_1}$ in the inner sum gives the branch transmittances in the first processing stage; $W_2^{k_2 n_2}$

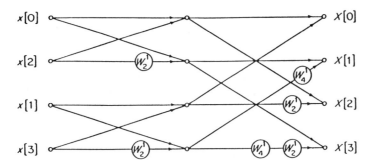

Figure 3.4 The signal flow graph of figure 3.3 recast in terms of W_2 and twiddle factors

corresponds to transmittances in the second stage, together with twiddle factors $W_4^{k_1 n_2}$.

Of course, we have developed all the above ideas in relation to one simple radix-2 FFT decomposition, and must be careful not to jump to too many conclusions! The basic ideas will be expanded in the next section, where we design several alternative types of FFT algorithm. In the meantime there are some further features which must be mentioned.

The first of these concerns the important notion of an *FFT butterfly*. The 2-point transforms on the left-hand side of figures 3.3 and 3.4 each involve just one addition and one subtraction. This can be viewed as the basic computational unit of the FFT, and is represented by part (a) of figure 3.5. We have now indicated the subtraction by placing a '-1' against the appropriate branch. Because of its shape, the figure is known as a 'butterfly'. In some books and references the shape is simplified as in part (b) of the figure. Even without arrows or labels, it has the same interpretation.

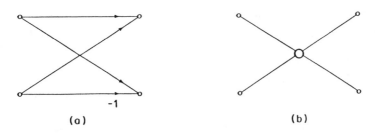

(a) (b)

Figure 3.5 (a) Basic FFT butterfly; (b) alternative butterfly symbol

Digital Signals, Processors and Noise

The basic FFT butterfly is also relevant to the second (and any further) processing stages, provided we include appropriate twiddle factors. Let us take the lower right-hand two-point DFT in figure 3.4 as an example. As already noted, its twiddle factors can be combined, giving the flow graph of part (a) of figure 3.6. This is now in the form of a single twiddle factor followed by the basic FFT butterfly, as shown in part (b). The same perspective can be applied to all the 2-point transforms in a signal flow graph, giving an FFT decomposition expressed entirely in terms of butterflies and twiddle factors. From the point of view of computational economy, this is very valuable.

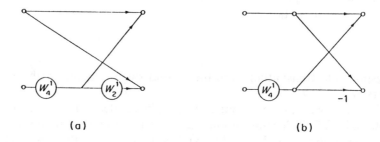

(a)   (b)

Figure 3.6   Separating a twiddle factor from a basic FFT butterfly

Closely related to twiddle factors and FFT butterflies is the idea of *in-place computation*. A basic FFT butterfly can be computed using a few elementary program instructions, storing the results back in the original data locations. This is because the data, once used, is not needed again. The idea can be extended to a complete signal flow graph, using the same (complex) data array throughout, and updating it stage-by-stage. Storage requirements are thereby minimised. However it is important to appreciate that such in-place computation requires either input or output data shuffling, to keep the nodes of each butterfly at the correct horizontal level in the flow graph.

Most FFT decompositions involve more than the two processing stages shown in figure 3.3 If we decompose an N-point DFT right down to 2-point DFTs, V processing stages are needed, where $V = \log_2 N$. Let us denote the complex data array resulting from the mth stage as $X_m(l)$, where $l = 0$, $1, 2 \ldots (N - 1)$, and $m = 1, 2, 3 \ldots V$. We can think of the input data (after shuffling) as being loaded initially into the array and denoted by $X_0(1)$. The general form of butterfly for the $(m + 1)$th stage of computation is then as shown in figure 3.7, where T_F denotes the appropriate twiddle factor. $X_{m+1}(p)$ overwrites $X_m(p)$, and so on. The figure is equivalent to the following equations, which are used over and over again:

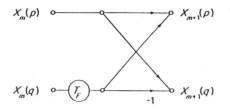

Figure 3.7   General form of butterfly and twiddle factor for a decimation-in-time FFT

$$X_{m+1}(p) = X_m(p) + T_F X_m(q)$$

$$X_{m+1}(q) = X_m(p) - T_F X_m(q) \tag{3.21}$$

In many practical implementations the twiddle factor multiplications are considered as part of the butterfly and absorbed within it. A common form of FFT program structure is based on three nested loops. The outer loop steps through the processing stages one at a time; the inner loops implement the butterfly and twiddle factor calculations. As with the standard DFT, various refinements and modifications are possible – including table look-ups, and algorithms designed for real data. The book by Burrus and Parks (see reference 9 in the Bibliography at the end of this book) gives a useful account, and lists a number of detailed FFT programs.

3.2.4   Decimation-in-time algorithms

There are various types of FFT algorithm based upon the same general approach – decomposition of a DFT into successively shorter DFTs. In this section we continue our account of decimation-in-time algorithms, starting with an 8-point FFT of the same general type as the 4-point example met previously. This will help consolidate basic ideas, preparing the ground for further concepts and discussion, and leading on to the alternative decimation-in-frequency designs which we describe in the next section.

An 8-point, radix-2, decimation-in-time FFT is defined by the following index-map equations:

$$n = 4n_1 + 2n_2 + n_3 \quad \text{and} \quad k = k_1 + 2k_2 + 4k_3 \tag{3.22}$$

with all six independent variables taken over the range 0 to 1. Since each index map now involves three independent variables, we cannot construct the maps as we did in figure 3.2. Instead we may tabulate n and k as in figure 3.8. Comparing the two maps, we see that if k is taken through the

n_1	n_2	n_3	n
0	0	0	0
1	0	0	4
0	1	0	2
1	1	0	6
0	0	1	1
1	0	1	5
0	1	1	3
1	1	1	7

k_1	k_2	k_3	k
0	0	0	0
1	0	0	1
0	1	0	2
1	1	0	3
0	0	1	4
1	0	1	5
0	1	1	6
1	1	1	7

Figure 3.8   Index maps for an 8-point FFT

natural-order sequence 0 to 7, then the corresponding input sequence must be 0, 4, 2, 6, 1, 5, 3, 7.

The form of the DFT for $N = 8$ is

$$X[k] = \sum_{n=0}^{N-1} x[n] \, W_N^{kn} = \sum_{n=0}^{7} x[n] \, W_8^{kn} \tag{3.23}$$

Substituting for n using equation (3.22) we may write:

$$X = \sum_{n_3=0}^{1} \sum_{n_2=0}^{1} \sum_{n_1=0}^{1} x \, W_8^{k(4n_1+2n_2+n_3)}$$

$$= \sum_{n_3=0}^{1} W_8^{kn_3} \sum_{n_2=0}^{1} W_8^{2kn_2} \sum_{n_1=0}^{1} x \, W_8^{4kn_1} \tag{3.24}$$

This equation could be expanded to define the 2-point DFTs relevant to three processing stages (compare with equations (3.15) and (3.16)). However the result is rather cumbersome, so we will infer the form of the signal flow graph directly.

The inner sum over n_1 represents the first stage of processing. Branch transmittances, given by $W_8^{4kn_1}$, take values W_8^0, W_8^4, W_8^8, W_8^{12} . . . and so on. Interpreted modulo-8 they all become either W_8^0 or W_8^4, and are shown on the left-hand side of figure 3.9.

The middle sum over n_2 represents the second stage. Branch transmittances, given by $W_8^{2kn_2}$, are again interpreted modulo-8. Similarly, the outer sum over n_3 gives the third stage transmittances which vary between W_8^0 and W_8^7. Comparing the overall structure of the graph with figure 3.3, we see many similarities. Note how the vertical span of individual 2-point DFTs doubles each time we enter a new processing stage.

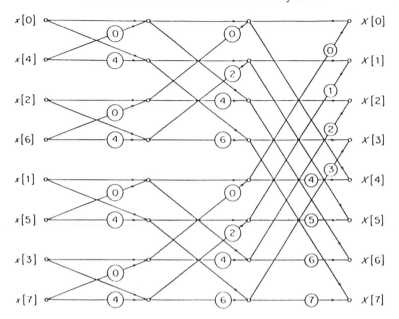

Figure 3.9   8-point, radix-2, decimation-in-time FFT with shuffled input and natural-order output. Branch transmittances are expressed as powers of W_8

Let us now redraw the graph in terms of FFT butterflies and twiddle factors. First, we recall that the basic butterfly incorporates a subtraction, and we note that $W_8^4 = -1$. Therefore if we have a transmittance equal to (say) W_8^6, we express it as $W_8^4 W_8^2 = (-1)W_8^2$. The '-1' becomes part of the butterfly, leaving W_8^2 as a twiddle factor. Examination of all the transmittances shows that one twiddle factor is sufficient for each 2-point DFT, provided it is taken *outside* the basic butterfly. The resulting scheme is then as shown in figure 3.10. Since many of the twiddle factors are $W_8^0 = 1$, they could be omitted; however their presence helps underline the structure and symmetry of the graph. Note that although there are twelve twiddle factors in all, only two of them (W_8^1 and W_8^3) require complex multiplications. Such decimation-in-time schemes are among the most widely-used of all FFTs, and come into the class of *Cooley–Tukey* algorithms first described in the mid-1960s.

The butterfly–twiddle factor arrangement of figure 3.10 can also be related to the index maps for n and k – very much as we did for the 4-point FFT in the previous section. Substituting for n and k from equation (3.22), the 8-point DFT becomes

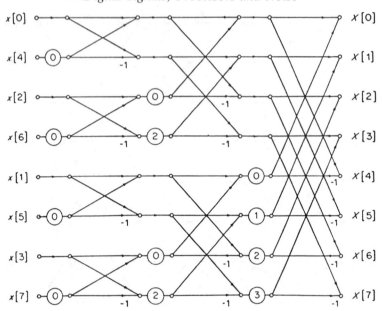

Figure 3.10   Figure 3.9 recast in terms of basic butterflies and twiddle
              factors

$$X = \sum_{n=0}^{7} x \, W_8^{kn} = \sum_{n_3=0}^{1} \sum_{n_2=0}^{1} \sum_{n_1=0}^{1} x \, W_8^{(k_1+2k_2+4k_3)(4n_1+2n_2+n_3)} \quad (3.25)$$

The index of W_8 multiplies out to give

$$(16k_3n_1 + 8k_2n_1 + 8k_3n_2 + 4k_1n_1 + 4k_2n_2 + 4k_3n_3 + 2k_1n_2 + 2k_2n_3$$
$$+ k_1n_3) \qquad\qquad (3.26)$$

Evaluated modulo-8, the first three of these terms always produce
$W_8^0 = 1$, and do not affect the computation. We therefore have

$$X = \sum_{n_3=0}^{1} \sum_{n_2=0}^{1} \sum_{n_1=0}^{1} x \, W_8^{4k_1n_1} W_8^{4k_2n_2} W_8^{4k_3n_3} W_8^{2k_1n_2} W_8^{2k_2n_3} W_8^{k_1n_3}$$

$$= \sum_{n_3=0}^{1} W_8^{n_3(2k_2+k_1)} W_8^{4k_3n_3} \sum_{n_2=0}^{1} W_8^{2k_1n_2} W_8^{4k_2n_2} \sum_{n_1=0}^{1} x \, W_8^{4k_1n_1} \qquad (3.27)$$

The three summations correspond to the three stages of processing in the signal flow graph. In each case there are transmittances equal to a power of W_8^4. These always have values ± 1 and are incorporated in the basic FFT butterfly. The extra terms – $W_8^{2k_1n_2}$ in the second stage, $W_8^{n_3(2k_2+k_1)}$ in the third stage – represent the twiddle factors.

As noted previously, in-place FFT algorithms require data shuffling to ensure horizontal alignment of the input and output nodes of each butterfly. So far we have assumed a shuffled input, with the output in natural order. However the opposite is also possible – a natural-order input and shuffled output. Perhaps the easiest way to explain this is to treat a signal flow graph as a network with a defined *topology*. Its nodes can be arranged in any way we please, as long as we use the same interconnections between nodes, and same transmittances. It is only the order of data storage and processing which changes. Applying this idea to our 8-point FFT, we can readily generate the alternative form shown in figure 3.11. First we enter the input data $x[0]$ to $x[7]$ in natural order down the left-hand side, and the output in shuffled order on the right. It is now quite easy to fill in the various branches and transmittances for the first and third processing stages, making exactly the same connections as in figure 3.10. Finally, we add the branches and transmittances for the second stage.

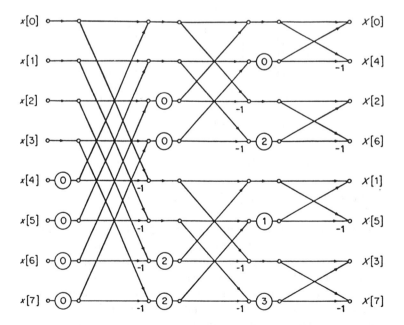

Figure 3.11   Alternative form of the FFT shown in figure 3.10: an in-place algorithm with natural-order input and shuffled output

It is worth emphasising that figure 3.11 is simply a rearrangement of figure 3.10. The same computations are required in both cases, and we still have an in-place, decimation-in-time algorithm.

It is also quite possible to reorganise the signal flow graph to give both input and output in natural order. However the in-place nature of the algorithm must be sacrificed, because the horizontal levels of the butterfly nodes cannot be preserved. Schemes of this type are described in references 4 and 5 in the Bibliography at the end of this book.

So far we have defined the sequences required for shuffled data by referring to the appropriate index maps. An alternative, widely-used technique is known as *bit-reversal*. Suppose, once again, that we wish to define the shuffled input sequence of figure 3.9. We first express the indices of $x[0]$ to $x[7]$ as 3-bit codes; reversal of the bit pattern then yields the shuffled sequence, as shown in figure 3.12. Bit reversal is a quick and convenient way of assessing shuffled sequences, and may be used with a wide range of FFTs.

Now that we have covered the basic notions of radix-2, decimation-in-time FFTs, it is time to turn to an alternative group of algorithms based on the *decimation-in-frequency* approach.

Natural-order data	3-bit code	Bit-reversed code	Shuffled data
$x[0]$	0 0 0	0 0 0	$x[0]$
$x[1]$	0 0 1	1 0 0	$x[4]$
$x[2]$	0 1 0	0 1 0	$x[2]$
$x[3]$	0 1 1	1 1 0	$x[6]$
$x[4]$	1 0 0	0 0 1	$x[1]$
$x[5]$	1 0 1	1 0 1	$x[5]$
$x[6]$	1 1 0	0 1 1	$x[3]$
$x[7]$	1 1 1	1 1 1	$x[7]$

Figure 3.12   Shuffling by bit-reversal

3.2.5   *Decimation-in-frequency algorithms*

The important class of decimation-in-frequency FFTs are in a sense the exact 'opposite', or *dual*, of the decimation-in-time algorithms we have examined so far. It should perhaps cause no surprise that the decimation-in-time approach has a frequency-domain counterpart; it is simply a consequence of the essential symmetry of Fourier Transformation.

We have already seen how a decimation-in-time FFT divides the input data into interleaved subsequences for the purposes of processing. A decimation-in-frequency algorithm uses the opposite approach: the output is decimated, rather than the input. To see how this is done, we will start with a simple 4-point DFT – very much as we did for decimation-in-time algorithms in the previous sections.

As before, an in-place algorithm requires data shuffling, which can be either on the input or the output side. You may remember that our initial treatment of decimation-in-time algorithms assumed *input* data shuffling. So to emphasise the dual nature of the decimation-in-frequency approach, we will start with an FFT which uses *output* shuffling.

A 4-point decimation-in-frequency FFT may be defined by the following index equations for n and k:

$$n = n_1 + 2n_2 \quad \text{and} \quad k = 2k_1 + k_2 \tag{3.28}$$

Substituting for n in the basic 4-point DFT equation, we readily obtain:

$$X = \sum_{n_2=0}^{1} W_4^{2kn_2} \sum_{n_1=0}^{1} x\, W_4^{kn_1}$$

$$= 1 \sum_{n_1=0}^{1} x\, W_4^{kn_1} + W_4^{2k} \sum_{n_1=0}^{1} x\, W_4^{kn_1} \tag{3.29}$$

Each of these sums has the general form of a 2-point DFT. You may like to compare with equation (3.15). Both equations represent the same overall computation, but they are arranged rather differently. The relevant index maps are shown in figure 3.13. We see that if $n_2 = 0$ then $n = 0$, 1 when $n_1 = 0$, 1; and if $n_2 = 1$ then $n = 2$, 3 when $n_1 = 0$, 1. Hence equation (3.29) is equivalent to

$$X = \{x[0] + x[1]\, W_4^k\} + W_4^{2k}\{x[2] + x[3]\, W_4^k\} \tag{3.30}$$

Interpreting the indices of W_4 modulo-4, and remembering that $W_4^0 = 1$, equation (3.30) may be represented by the signal flow graph of figure 3.14. Note that the output is shuffled – and also decimated, since $X[0]$ and $X[2]$ are paired, and so are $X[1]$ and $X[3]$. The graph looks like a 'back-to-front' version of the decimation-in-time FFT of figure 3.3.

$n_1 =$	0	1
$n_2 = 0$	0	1
$n_2 = 1$	2	3

$k_1 =$	0	1
$k_2 = 0$	0	2
$k_2 = 1$	1	3

Figure 3.13   Index maps for a 4-point decimation-in-frequency FFT

Digital Signals, Processors and Noise

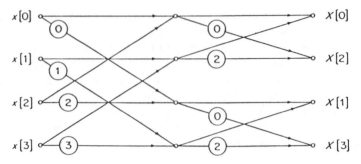

Figure 3.14   4-point, in-place, decimation-in-freqency FFT with natural-order input and shuffled output

To rearrange figure 3.14 in the form of FFT butterflies and twiddle factors, we need to combine pairs of branch transmittances which travel *towards*, rather than away from, a given node – in contrast to the decimation-in-time case. Therefore the twiddle factors must now *follow* the butterflies, rather than precede them, giving the basic 2-point butterfly and twiddle factor combination in figure 3.15. The corresponding equations are

$$X_{m+1}(p) = X_m(p) + X_m(q)$$

$$X_{m+1}(q) = \{X_m(p) - X_m(q)\}T_F \tag{3.31}$$

The rearrangement of figure 3.14 is shown in figure 3.16.

Having outlined the decimation-in-frequency approach, we can apply it to a more complicated example – an 8-point FFT which is the counterpart of the decimation-in-time algorithm explored in the previous section.

The index map equations for an 8-point, radix-2, in-place, decimation-in-frequency FFT are

$$n = n_1 + 2n_2 + 4n_3 \quad \text{and} \quad k = 4k_1 + 2k_2 + k_3 \tag{3.32}$$

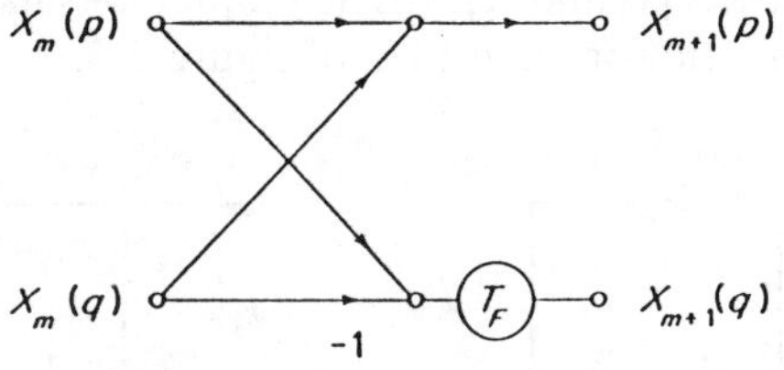

Figure 3.15   General form of butterfly and twiddle factor for a decimation-in-frequency FFT

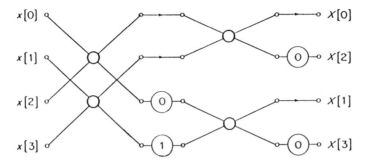

Figure 3.16   Figure 3.14 redrawn in terms of butterflies and twiddle factors

Note that these are the same as the decimation-in-time case, but with n and k interchanged. Hence the shuffling sequence – applied in this case to the output – must also be the same. The FFT decomposition may be expressed as

$$X = \sum_{n_3=0}^{1} \sum_{n_2=0}^{1} \sum_{n_1=0}^{1} x\, W_8^{k(n_1+2n_2+4n_3)}$$

$$= \sum_{n_3=0}^{1} W_8^{4kn_3} \sum_{n_2=0}^{1} W_8^{2kn_2} \sum_{n_1=0}^{1} x\, W_8^{kn_1} \qquad (3.33)$$

The first processing stage (corresponding to the inner sum over n_1) has branch transmittances equal to powers of W_8^1; in the second stage they are powers of W_8^2; and in the third stage, of W_8^4. The general form of the flow graph must be like figure 3.14. In particular, the final processing stage must involve basic two-point transforms on adjacent (shuffled) values of X. If we move back through stage 2 to stage 1, the vertical span of the 2-point transforms will double at each stage. These considerations lead to the signal flow graph of figure 3.17, in which all branch transmittances are expressed modulo-8.

To recast the graph in terms of butterflies and twiddle factors, we combine the transmittances of branches travelling towards a given node. For example, the node marked N' at the bottom of figure 3.17 has two input branches with transmittances W_8^3 and W_8^7. Since the basic FFT butterfly involves a subtraction, we write W_8^7 as $W_8^4 W_8^3 = (-1)W_8^3$. The W_8^3 term becomes the twiddle factor common to the two input branches. The overall signal flow graph is redrawn in figure 3.18 using the simplified form of butterfly schematic.

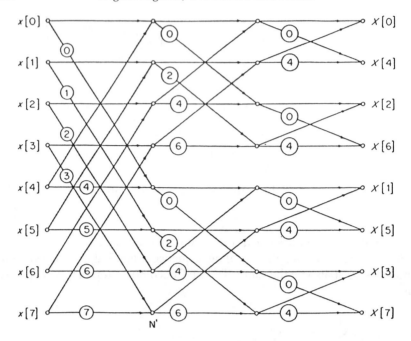

Figure 3.17   8-point decimation-in-frequency FFT with branch transmittances expressed as powers of W_8

There are several possible forms for a given decimation-in-frequency
FFT. As long as we preserve node interconnections and branch transmittances, the flow graph can be rearranged in any way we wish. Figure 3.19
shows one of the alternative forms – an in-place version with shuffled input
and natural-order output.

We should say a few words about computing the inverse Discrete
Fourier Transform (IDFT), given by equation (3.2). Note that it is
identical to the DFT apart from a $1/N$ scaling factor and change of sign in
the index of W_N. It follows that an FFT algorithm can be used to compute
the IDFT, if we divide the result by N and use powers of W_N^{-1} rather than
W_N. This means that a given algorithm can be used to process either
time-domain or frequency-domain data, with only very minor modifications. For example, the 8-point decimation-in-time FFT of figure 3.10 is
readily adapted to give an 8-point decimation-in-frequency inverse FFT.

Another general point is that we have concentrated so far on the
widely-used type of radix-2 FFT, in which an N-point DFT is decomposed
right down to 2-point transforms. However, radix-4 (or higher radix)
algorithms may be attractive for implementing FFTs efficiently on special-
purpose DSP hardware. The basic idea of a radix-4 FFT is to decompose
the overall DFT only as far as 4-point DFTs, using a 4-point transform as

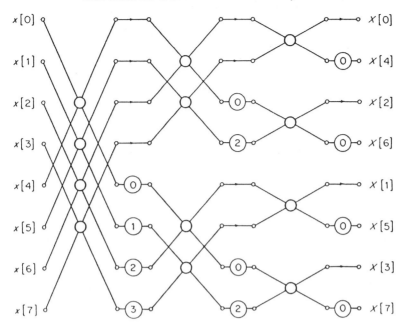

Figure 3.18   Figure 3.17 redrawn in terms of butterflies and twiddle factors

the basic computational unit, and incorporating twiddle factors where necessary. Obviously, the 4-point transform is rather more complicated than the 2-point butterfly we have used previously; but it requires only additions, subtractions and changes between real and imaginary.

One danger of illustrating FFT algorithms with 2-point, 4-point and 8-point signal flow graphs is that we tend to forget the lengthy DFTs used in practical DSP. Quite often we need to transform signals with many hundreds, or thousands, of sample values. In such cases higher-radix FFTs are a genuine option. On other occasions it may be best to use a mixed-radix algorithm: for example, a lengthy DFT might be decomposed into a mixture of 2-point and 4-point DFTs. A further aspect of FFT design concerns transform lengths which are not integer powers of 2. As we mentioned earlier, the index-mapping approach is particularly useful in such cases. These and other more advanced FFT topics are covered in several of the references given in the Bibliography at the end of this book.

3.2.6   FFT processing

Our next aim is to outline some important application areas of the FFT, and explain the practical issues which arise. In particular we shall comment

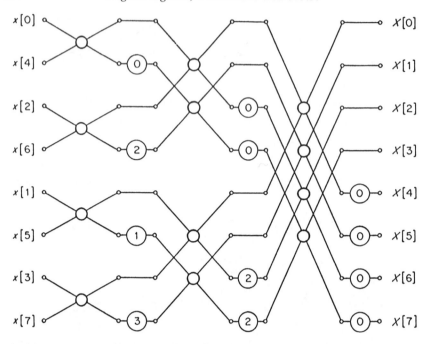

Figure 3.19   An alternative form of figure 3.18 with shuffled input and natural-order output

on *digital spectral analysis* – using the FFT to explore the spectral properties of signals and processors. In the next section we will look at *fast convolution* – a powerful frequency-domain alternative to the time-domain filtering techniques described in chapter 2.

We start by describing a general-purpose FFT program which can be used to demonstrate various aspects of FFT processing. Computer Program 6 in appendix A is a radix-2, in-place FFT of the decimation-in-time variety, with shuffled input and natural-order output. It can cope with DFTs and IDFTs of any length equal to an integer power of 2, and is based on three nested program loops – a fairly standard programming technique covered by references 6 and 9 in the Bibliography at the end of this book.

The program begins by defining storage arrays for the real and imaginary parts of the input data, the length of the transform required (N), and the parameter $M = \log_2 N$. Two control parameters, T and D, determine whether a transform or inverse transform is performed. T sets the sign of the exponential in DFT equation (3.1); D provides the $1/N$ scaling factor in IDFT equation (3.2). Thus if $T = 1$ and $D = 1$, we compute the transform; if $T = -1$ and $D = N$, the inverse transform. On the first 'pass' through the program, the transform is estimated. The result is normalised to a suitable peak value, then plotted on the screen. For ease of interpretation we have plotted just the magnitude of the transform; remember, however, that it is generally a complex function, and that its real and imaginary parts remain stored in the relevant arrays.

We have previously emphasised that the process of inverse transformation is almost identical to that of transformation. Our program demonstrates this by inverse-transforming the spectrum it has just calculated, using a second 'pass' with $T = 1$ and $D = N$. The result is also plotted on the screen.

The complete screen plot for a suitable input signal – a 'rectangular pulse' 32 samples wide – is shown in figure 3.20. In this case the total length of the transform (N) is 512. Part (a) shows the input, and part (b) the magnitude of the transform, comprising 512 discrete spectral coefficients. Note that since $x[n]$ is real, the spectrum shows the usual mirror-image pattern. Its halfway point, the 256th spectral coefficient, corresponds to $\Omega = \pi$ in other frequency plots in this book. Part (c) shows the signal recovered by a final inverse transformation. The process has indeed come full circle.

Remember that parts (b) and (c) of the figure represent magnitudes. Since we have chosen a signal with only positive sample values for this illustration, parts (a) and (c) of the figure are identical. In general,

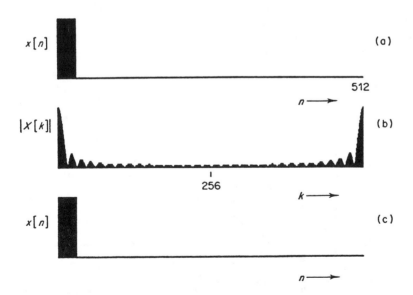

Figure 3.20   (a) A signal $x[n]$; (b) its spectral magnitude found using the FFT; and (c) the signal recovered by inverse transformation (*abscissa: 512 samples*)

however, (c) would be a rectified version of (a). Bearing this point in mind, you may like to try the program with other forms of input signal.

It is interesting to assess the speed of such an FFT program, compared with a direct implementation of the DFT. Based upon the number of multiplications involved, we expect the speed advantage of the FFT to be about $N/\log_2 N$ – a value widely quoted in the DSP literature (of course, many other arithmetic and control operations are needed as well, so the estimate is only approximate). In figure 3.21 we show results of some actual speed tests on a personal computer. Much less emphasis should be placed on the absolute computation times given than on their relative values, because the speeds of different computers vary widely, and improve year by year. But the results are broadly in line with the expected $N/\log_2 N$ factor, and confirm a growing advantage for the FFT as transform lengths increase.

We now turn to the FFT processing topic mentioned above – digital spectral analysis. Breaking a digital signal down into its spectral components is a very valuable technique in many branches of engineering and applied science. The basic assumption behind such analysis is that a frequency-domain description is likely to reveal information not apparent in the time-domain signal. Another type of application involves investigating linear systems or processors. By disturbing such a system with a suitable input signal and performing a frequency analysis of the response, we can define its frequency-dependent properties. Such techniques are widely used for testing electronic circuits and filters, for analysing vibrations in structures, and in radar, sonar and seismology. Some commercially available test instruments incorporate FFT analysers for this purpose.

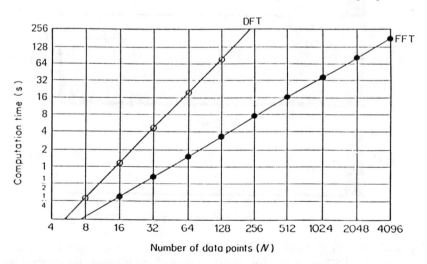

Figure 3.21   DFT and FFT computation times on a personal computer

In general, FFT analysis yields a set of spectral coefficients which may be regarded as samples of the underlying continuous spectral function – or as harmonics of a repetitive version of the same signal. We saw in section 1.4.1 that end-on-end repetition of a signal $x[n]$ causes no sudden discontinuities if all its frequency components have an integral number of periods within the transform length (N). Each component then occupies a definite harmonic frequency, corresponding to a single spectral coefficient. However the situation is more complicated when $x[n]$ contains frequencies which do not meet this criterion. Repetition causes time-domain discontinuities, leading to spectral spreading or leakage in the frequency domain. We previously demonstrated the effect for a 64-point transform in figure 1.17.

This matter is of such significance for spectral analysis that we illustrate it again in figure 3.22, using our FFT program (with a changed input signal, and omitting the inverse transform). The top of the figure shows the signal:

$$x[n] = 0.1 \sin\left(\frac{2\pi n}{512} 16\right) + 0.2 \sin\left(\frac{2\pi n}{512} 53.5\right)$$

$$+ 0.15 \cos\left(\frac{2\pi n}{512} 211.25\right), \quad 1 \leq n \leq 512 \tag{3.34}$$

The first component corresponds exactly to the 16th harmonic of the Fourier Series, and produces a single spectral line. The second component displays a double peak at the 53rd and 54th harmonic frequencies, with spectral leakage to either side. And the third component, whose frequency is closer to the 211th harmonic than the 212th, gives a relatively large 211th coefficient – and there is again spectral leakage.

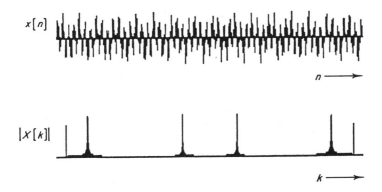

Figure 3.22   Fourier transformation of a signal containing both harmonic and non-harmonic components (*abscissa: 512 samples*)

There are two rather different, and complementary, ways of explaining such spectral leakage. Firstly, we may think of it as the frequency-domain counterpart of the discontinuities in the time domain caused by repetition. The other explanation, which gives valuable insight into the nature of discrete Fourier transformation, is to regard the DFT (or FFT) as a type of *filtering process*. A DFT behaves like a set of elementary bandpass filters which split the signal into its various frequency components. This is illustrated for the simple case of an 8-point transform ($N = 8$) in part (a) of figure 3.23. The frequency range $0 \leqslant \Omega \leqslant 2\pi$ is effectively divided into 8 overlapping bands, and the 'amount' of input signal falling within each band is estimated.

Note that the peak response of each filter coincides with zero response in its neighbours. Thus, for example, a sinusiodal input signal at the centre-frequency of filter no. 3 would give a peak output from that filter, but zero output from all the others. Not surprisingly, it turns out that the eight centre-frequencies shown in the figure correspond exactly with the harmonics of the 8-point transform.

Actually this is not quite the whole story, because each elementary filter characteristic has substantial sidelobes to either side of its main lobe. As transform length increases, each characteristic tends to a sinc function. We show such a function in part (b). The width of its main lobe is $4\pi/N$ radians; the sidelobes are $2\pi/N$ radians wide, with amplitudes decreasing away from the centre frequency Ω_c. Note that the zero-crossings of the sinc function coincide with the centre-frequencies of the other filters. Thus, once again, a signal component at an exact harmonic frequency only produces an output from one of the filters.

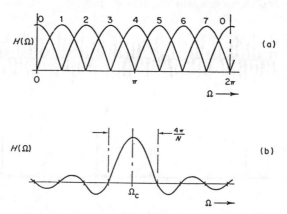

Figure 3.23   An 8-point FFT considered as a set of elementary bandpass filters

If a component is displaced from the filter's centre-frequency, it gives a smaller peak response, plus a whole series of sidelobe responses from adjacent filters. This is the spectral leakage effect illustrated in figure 3.22.

Spectral leakage is generally present when dealing with practical signals, and may lead to problems of interpretation. It is therefore common practice to taper the original signal before transformation, reducing discontinuities at its edges. We do this by multiplying by a suitable window function, causing the spectrum of the 'raw' signal $x[n]$ to be convolved with that of the window. By choosing a suitable window, we can arrange that the convolution reduces the undesirable effects of spectral leakage. The technique closely parallels the use of windows in non-recursive filter design, as described in section 2.1.3, and is more fully covered in reference 4 in the Bibliography at the end of this book.

3.2.7 Fast convolution

Another valuable use of FFT algorithms is in implementing frequency-domain equivalents of the time-domain digital filters described in chapter 2. Rather than *convolve* an input signal with the impulse response of the desired filter, we transform the signal using an FFT and then *multiply* it by the equivalent frequency response. A final inverse transform yields the filtered signal. Although the method sounds tortuous, it often proves faster than time-domain convolution. This is due to the relative simplicity of multiplication, and the speed with which an FFT can perform the necessary transforms and inverse transforms.

Quite often we start with an impulse response rather than a frequency response. It is then necessary to transform the impulse response into the frequency domain as well. The complete filtering process, shown in figure 3.24, is known as *fast convolution*.

We have previously emphasised that FFT algorithms assume the functions being transformed are periodic, with period N. It follows that fast convolution gives an output signal $y[n]$ which is the periodic, or *circular*, convolution of $x[n]$ and $h[n]$. However in digital filtering we require *linear* convolution; that is, we need to convolve an aperiodic input signal and

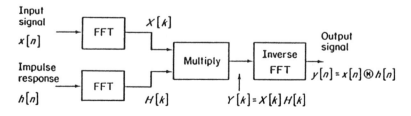

Figure 3.24   Fast convolution

impulse response to produce an aperiodic output. Fortunately, it turns out that one period of the output signal derived by circular convolution gives the correct result, provided we extend the lengths of the transforms in figure 3.24 using an appropriate amount of *zero-filling*.

This is illustrated by figures 3.25 and 3.26. Figure 3.25 shows a circular convolution of two functions $x[n]$ and $h[n]$, producing the function $y[n]$. All are assumed periodic. We have chosen 'rectangular pulses' for $x[n]$ and $h[n]$ because they are convenient for illustration. All the functions have 9 samples per period, and we see that in this case $y[n]$ consists of overlapping 'flat-topped triangles', shown dotted. The overlap occurs because the repetitions of $x[n]$ and $h[n]$ are close together, with few zero values between them. However if we increase the period by inserting more zeros, the overlap disappears. Each period of $y[n]$ then has an identical form to the required linear convolution of non-repetitive versions of $x[n]$ and $h[n]$ – as shown in figure 3.26.

In general we can avoid overlap in a circular convolution of two functions with N_1 and N_2 non-zero samples per period, provided we make the period $N \leqslant (N_1 + N_2 - 1)$. Fast concolution then gives the result required in digital filtering.

A rough estimate of the speed advantage of fast convolution over a normal time-domain convolution can be made as follows. Fast convolution requires two N-point FFTs, and one N-point inverse FFT. These three operations involve about $3N\log_2 N$ complex multiplications and additions/subtractions. Also, N complex multiplications are required to form the product $X[k]$ $H[k]$. A normal time-domain convolution requires about $N_1 N_2$ real multiplications and additions. For simplicity let us assume that

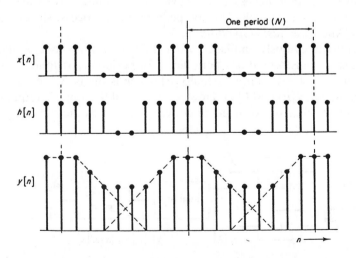

Figure 3.25   Circular (periodic) convolution

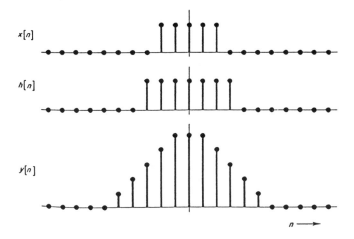

Figure 3.26   Linear (aperiodic) convolution

multiplications take up most of the computing time, and that a complex multiplication needs twice as long as a real one. If N_1 and N_2 are about half the transform length N, the speed advantage of fast convolution should be approximately:

$$\frac{N_1 N_2}{2(3N\log_2 N + N)} \approx \frac{N^2}{8(3N\log_2 N + N)} \tag{3.35}$$

Values of this function are given in the accompanying table. Note that the expected advantage of fast convolution increases rapidly with transform length. It is also important to remember that we often wish to work with real functions of time, for which only half the complete transforms need be calculated. Furthermore, zero-filling of $x[n]$ and $h[n]$ means that many of the multiplications do not, in fact, have to be carried out. Efficient algorithms take such factors into account, and give further speed increases.

Length of transforms (N)	Speed advantage
128	0.73
256	1.3
1024	4.1
4096	14

The screen plots in figure 3.27 illustrate the various stages of a complete fast convolution performed on a personal computer, for a 'rectangular pulse' input signal $x[n]$, and an impulse response $h[n]$ representing a

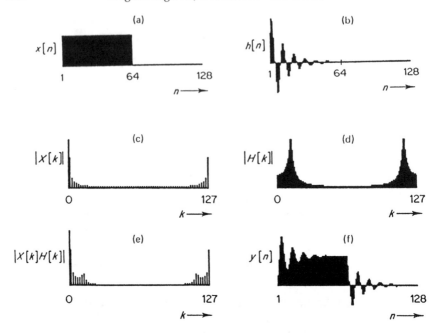

Figure 3.27 Illustration of fast convolution

bandpass filter. Both functions are zero-filled up to the transform length $N = 128$ (see parts (a) and (b) of the figure). In parts (c) and (d) we see the respective spectral functions (just the magnitudes are plotted); in part (e) their product; and in part (f) the output signal $y[n]$ obtained by inverse transformation.

So far we have implied that the input signal and impulse response contain roughly the same number of samples, and that they are zero-filled up to the same transform length ($N = 128$ in figure 3.27). However in practice it is more usual to encounter long input signals or data sequences, and relatively short impulse responses. This makes it uneconomic in terms of computing time (and storage) to use the same lengthy transforms for both functions. Furthermore, in real-time applications the use of a very long transform for $x[n]$ may introduce an unacceptable processing delay.

The problem may be overcome by *segmenting* the input signal into sections of manageable length, performing a fast convolution on each section, and combining the outputs. Two approaches, known as *overlap–add* and *overlap–save* (or *select–save*) are commonly employed. In over-lap–add, the input signal is split into adjacent, non-overlapping segments. Although the time-domain spreading effect of convolution means that the corresponding output segments overlap, it is found that the correct overall output signal $y[n]$ is given by a straightforward superposition. In the alternative overlap–save method, the input signal is split into overlapping segments equal to the chosen transform length N. The overall output signal may then be obtained by discarding some samples from each output segment, and concatenating the rest. Details of the two approaches are given in, for example, reference 5 in the Bibliography at the end of this book.

It is sometimes implied that fast convolution is the answer to every DSP designer's prayer. However, a word of scepticism is in order. While it is undoubtedly true that the advent of fast and efficient FFT algorithms in the 1960s had a profound influence on DSP, we must not assume that the frequency-domain approach to digital filtering is necessarily superior. If we have the option of using a recursive filter with just a few multiplier coefficients, the speed advantage may well tip back in favour of a time-domain operation.

Problems

Section 3.1

3.1. Explain the distinction between:

(a) the discrete Fourier series and the DFT
(b) the discrete-time version of the Fourier Transform and the DFT.

What is the justification for representing an N-sample digital signal by N spectral coefficients?

3.2. An N-sample signal $x[n]$ has the DFT $X[k]$. Write down expressions for the DFTs of signals:

(a) $3x[n]$
(b) $x[n-2]$
(c) $2x[n] + x[n+1]$
(d) $x[n]\,x[n-1]$

where all time shifts are assumed periodic.

3.3. Two real signals have the following sample values:

(a) $1, -1$
(b) $1, 2, 1, 3$.

Estimate the real and imaginary parts of their DFT coefficients $X[k]$.

3.4. The signal $x[n] = \cos(18\pi n/40)$ is applied to a 40-point DFT.

(a) Which coefficients have the largest magnitudes?
(b) What are the magnitudes of $X[0]$ and $X[39]$?

3.5. Tabulate values of W_N^{kn} for a 4-point DFT, with n and k taken over the range 0 to 3.

3.6. A 16-point, radix-2, in-place FFT algorithm has the following index map equations:

$$n = 8n_1 + 4n_2 + 2n_3 + n_4$$
$$k = k_1 + 2k_2 + 4k_3 + 8k_4$$

with all independent variables taken between 0 and 1. Construct index maps for n and k.

The FFT is to be implemented using shuffled input data and a natural-order output. Define the shuffled input sequence using (a) the index maps, and (b) the bit-reversal technique.

3.7. Use the bit-reversal technique to define the shuffle sequence for a 32-point in-place FFT algorithm.

3.8. Explain the essential differences between decimation-in-time and decimation-in-frequency FFT algorithms.

Section 3.2

3.9. Computer Program 6 in appendix A is a general-purpose, radix-2 FFT which can readily be modified for different lengths of transform and input signal. Change the program to accommodate the following:

(a) transform length $N = 512$; input signal given by

$$x[n] = 1, \quad 1 \leqslant n \leqslant 64$$
$$= 0, \quad \text{elsewhere.}$$

(b) transform length $N = 512$; input signal given by

$$x[n] = 1, \quad n = 1, 3, 5, \ldots 63$$
$$= 0.2, \quad n = 2, 4, 6, \ldots 64$$
$$= 0, \quad \text{elsewhere}$$

(c) transform length $N = 256$; input signal given by

$$x[n] = 0.2 \sin\left(\frac{2\pi n}{256} 9\right) + 0.15 \cos\left(\frac{2\pi n}{256} 100\right),$$

$$1 \leqslant n \leqslant 256$$

Study the screen plots in each case, making sure you can explain their main features. (*Note*: a real input signal should be loaded into array XR: also, remember that the final inverse transform is plotted as a *magnitude*.)

3.10. A 60 Hz sinusoidal signal is sampled at 500 samples per second, and analysed using a 64-point FFT.

(a) Which spectral coefficient will be the largest?
(b) Which coefficient will be the next largest, and what is its relative size, in dB, compared with the coefficient in part (a)?
(c) Find the sampling rate closest to 500 samples per second which will eliminate spectral leakage.

3.11. (a) A portion of a music signal is sampled at 44 kHz and analysed using a 2048-point FFT. Approximately what spectral resolution in Hz is provided by the transform?
(b) If a 256-point DFT or FFT is considered as a set of elementary bandpass filters, what is the width of each main lobe in the variable Ω (radians)?
(c) The sampling interval in part (b) is 1 second. What is the frequency interval in Hz between each filter's centre-frequency and the centre of its first sidelobe?

3.12. Calculate and plot the values of a 32-point data window with a half-Hamming taper over the first and last five values (that is, the central untapered portion is 22 points long).

Use the values as input data to the FFT program in appendix A (Computer Program 6), with a transform length $N = 256$ and zero-filling. Hence plot the window's spectral function. Comment on its merits as an FFT data window, compared with a 32-point rectangular ('do nothing') window.

3.13. Specify one period of the function obtained by circular convolution of the periodic functions $x[n]$ and $h[n]$ illustrated in figure P3.13.

Also perform a linear convolution of $x[n]$ and $h[n]$, assuming them to be aperiodic.

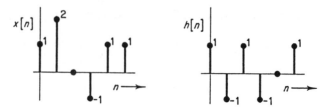

Figure P3.13

If $x[n]$ and $h[n]$ represent the aperiodic input signal and impulse response of a digital processor, under what conditions will the correct output signal $y[n]$ be obtained using the fast convolution technique?

4 Describing Random Sequences

4.1 Introduction

The signals we have already met in this book – including the impulses, steps and sinusoids described in chapter 1 – have precisely defined sample values and are generally referred to as *deterministic*. By contrast, the individual values of a *random* signal are not defined, nor can its future fluctuations be predicted with certainty. It is a central concept of modern communications that a signal can only convey useful information if it is, to some extent, unpredictable. For example, it would be pointless to transmit a periodic sinusoid through a communication channel, since once its frequency, amplitude and phase had been determined at the receiving end, no further information could be conveyed. But if we switch a sinusoidal tone on and off as in a Morse Code message, the person at the receiving end does not know what dot–dash sequence is to be sent next – and it is this very uncertainty which results in useful information flow.

Another way in which random functions enter signal theory is in terms of unwanted interference, or *noise*. Noise is present to some extent in all communication, measurement and recording situations. When picked up along a transmission path (for example a radio, optical fibre, or satellite link), it imposes a fundamental limit on information-carrying capacity. Noise is therefore a matter of great technical and economic importance.

In the field of DSP, we see that a knowledge of random functions is central to understanding both the information content of digital signals, and the properties of digital noise. The underlying principles are those of probability and statistics, which may be used to define useful *average measures* of random sample sequences.

Note that in principle a random sequence can represent either a digital signal, or digital noise, depending on one's viewpoint. If the sequence conveys useful information, it is a 'signal'; if it represents unwanted interference, it is 'noise'. Fortunately the statistical measures used to describe it are very similar in the two cases.

The type of situation we shall examine in this and the following chapter can be introduced with a simple computer illustration. You are probably aware that most high-level computer languages include a random number generator, which normally produces random numbers equally distributed in the range 0 to 1. A series of such numbers may be used to represent a random digital sequence, as shown in part (a) of figure 4.1. We may think of the sequence either as an information-bearing signal, or unwanted noise. In either case we may need to evaluate such statistical measures as its average (or mean, or dc) value, its mean-square value (or average power), and its variance (or ac power). We may also wish to examine whether successive sample values are truly independent, or whether the sequence is structured in some way. And we may well need to compute its average spectral properties – for example, if it represents a signal to be transmitted through a communication channel of limited bandwidth.

Other important questions arise if the sequence has been modified by linear processing – for example, by filtering. Some typical effects of filtering (in this example, we use a digital bandpass filter) are shown in part (b) of the figure. It is clear that the sequence now has a different distribution of amplitude values, including negative ones. In general its mean, mean square and variance are also modified. Furthermore it now has a distinctive time-domain structure, in which groups of positive and negative values tend to bunch together. In the frequency domain, we may expect spectral energy to be concentrated around the centre-frequency of the particular bandpass filter we have used. All these effects are potentially important – whether the sequence represents a useful signal or an unwanted noise – and we must be able to describe them quantitatively.

A further possibility is that such a sequence represents a wanted signal mixed with unwanted noise. In this case we may wish to process it with a filter which gives the best chance of recovering the signal. This is a

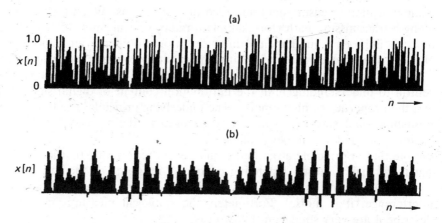

Figure 4.1   Random digital sequences: (a) produced by a random number generator, and (b) after bandpass filtering (*abscissae: 320 samples*)

particularly important type of problem which arises in many practical communications systems, including radar and sonar.

Although our treatment will be strictly introductory, our aim is to gain familiarity with the most widely-used statistical measures of random signals and noise, and – in the next chapter – some of the most important techniques for processing them with linear algorithms.

4.2 Basic measures of random sequences

4.2.1 Amplitude distribution

We are often interested in the distribution of amplitude values of a random digital sequence. For example, we may need to know the probability of finding a sample value at or above a certain level, or within a particular range. Such questions assume particular significance in *detection* situations, where the occurrence of a particular amplitude value (often a peak) is used to initiate some action or decision. Also, as we shall see in the next section, the amplitude distribution may be used to compute such widely used measures as the *mean*, *mean square* and *variance*.

In DSP we normally deal with discrete random variables in which the amplitude values are quantised. In other words they can only take on a countable number of values. An extreme example is a binary sequence, which can only take on two distinct values. But even when we are dealing with sampled analog signals in a digital computer, the number of possible amplitude values is finite, being limited by the numerical resolution (wordlength) of the machine. In such a situation, the familiar probability density function used to describe a continuous random variable is inappropriate. Instead, we define a *probability mass function* p_{x_n} as

$$p_{x_n} = \text{probability } \{x[n] = x_n\} \tag{4.1}$$

Thus p_{x_n} simply tells us the probability associated with each of the allowed values x_n of the sequence. An associated function, the *probability distribution function*, is defined as

$$p_{x_n} = \text{probability } \{x[n] \leqslant x_n\} = \sum_{-\infty}^{x_n} p_{x_n} \tag{4.2}$$

This takes a staircase form which is a running integral of the probability mass function. Discontinuities in the staircase occur at the allowable amplitude values of the sequence; and the height of a discontinuity represents the probability that the random sequence takes on that particular value.

Before going any further, we should make clear that such probability functions strictly relate to an infinite set, or *ensemble*, of random variables arising from a given random process. Here we wish to use them to describe the properties of a single sequence – an approach which involves certain assumptions. We will discuss these assumptions, and the ideas underlying them, in section 4.2.3.

You may find it helpful to have the above types of probability function illustrated by some simple examples.

To start with, let us consider a coin-tossing experiment. We toss the coin many times, generating a sequence of 'heads' and 'tails'. For convenience, let us denote these by +1 and −1 respectively, producing a random binary sequence. Assuming the coin is fair and unbiased, we expect both 'heads' and 'tails' to occur with probability 0.5. Hence the probability mass function is as shown in figure 4.2(a). The probability distribution function, which is its running integral, is shown alongside. Note that the sum of terms in the mass function must equal unity; and that the distribution function is of the *cumulative* type, starting at zero on the left-hand side, and ending at unity on the right.

As a second example, suppose we generate a random digital sequence by tossing a six-sided die. Assuming the die is fair, the probabilities associated with the six possible scores are all equal to 1/6, giving the probability functions shown in part (b) of the figure.

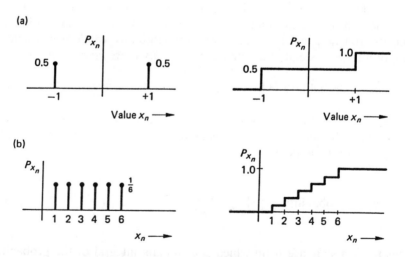

Figure 4.2   Probability functions associated with (a) coin-tossing, and (b) die-tossing

Finally, let us consider the form of these functions for the type of computer-generated random number sequence already illustrated in part (a) of figure 4.1. The values of this sequence fall anywhere in the range 0 to 1, with equal probability. At first sight, it might appear that there is an infinite number of possible values; but it is in fact limited by the resolution of the machine. For example, if the numbers are given to 6 decimal places (0.000000 to 0.999999), there are one million possible discrete values; and assuming the random number generator is 'fair', they will all have the probability 10^{-6}. We can hardly draw a probability mass function with a million separate probabilities on it, or a staircase distribution function with a million small steps – so we leave these figures to the imagination! (Incidentally, it is worth noting that the finite vertical resolution of the computer screen of part (a) of figure 4.1 has reduced the number of plotted values to about 100.)

All the amplitude distributions considered so far are *uniform* or *even*. That is, the same probability is associated with each of the possible sequence values. However it is important to realise that random sequences met in practical DSP are not generally of this type (one of the few common examples is quantisation noise associated with analog-to-digital conversion). Far more common is the *gaussian* distribution, named after the German mathematician Johann Gauss who investigated the random errors arising in astronomical observations. He considered the total error of a given measurement or observation to be the sum of a large number of individual random errors, each of which might be positive or negative in sign. He then showed mathematically that the probability density function of the total error takes the form:

$$p(x) = \frac{1}{\sigma \sqrt{(2\pi)}} \exp\left(\frac{-(x - \bar{x})^2}{2\sigma^2}\right) \tag{4.3}$$

where $\bar{x}$ is the mean value of the error variable, σ^2 is the variance and σ the standard deviation, and the constant $\sigma \sqrt{(2\pi)}$ is included to make the total area under the curve unity. In deriving this result, Gauss made no attempt to ascertain details of the small contributing errors, and his distribution has found a huge number of applications in different fields. It is therefore often called the *normal* distribution.

As far as DSP is concerned, any random sequence which is produced by superposition of many contributing processes is likely to have a gaussian form of amplitude distribution; for example, noise arising in digital communication systems is often of this type. Of course, we must now use a probability mass function in place of the density function of equation (4.3), obtaining a discrete function which follows a gaussian 'envelope'.

It is straightforward to generate a gaussian digital sequence on a computer, using a standard random number generator. It follows from

Gauss's result that if we add together many independent, uniformly-distributed, random numbers to form a new random number, and repeat the exercise over and over again to form a sequence, that sequence will be approximately gaussian. The more random numbers we add together, the better the approximation; however a compromise is clearly necessary, because we need to limit the amount of computation.

Computer Program 7 in appendix A illustrates the above points, and produces an estimate of two probability mass functions: one for a sequence whose values are uniformly distributed; the other for a gaussian sequence. It works as follows. First, it uses the computer's random number generator to produce a sequence of 3000 uniformly-distributed integer numbers in the range 0 to 300, and generates a histogram of 'scores' which builds up gradually on the screen. This is shown in part (a) of figure 4.3. Sequence values are plotted as the abscissa, and the number of times each occurs as the ordinate. The latter is therefore an indication of relative probability, and we see that it is indeed more or less uniform (of course, in a limited 'trial' we can only hope to get a result whose shape *tends towards* the underlying probability distribution).

The program next generates a gaussian sequence, also with 3000 sample values. Each is formed by adding together 30 uniformly-distributed random numbers in the range 0 to 1 (giving a random number in the range 0 to 30), and then multiplying by 10 to give a number in the range 0 to 300 (to allow comparison with part (a) of the figure). Once again a histogram

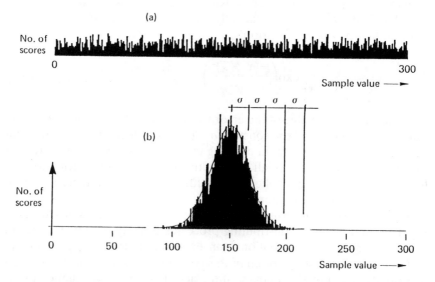

Figure 4.3   Estimates of probability mass functions for (a) a uniform distribution, and (b) a gaussian distribution (*abscissae: 301 samples*)

of scores is generated, as shown in part (b). We notice straight away that although the complete range 0 to 300 is theoretically possible, in fact the numbers almost all fall between about 100 and 200. The clustering of values around the mean (in this case 150), with a rapid fall-off towards the 'tails', is typical of a gaussian distribution. In our example it would be extremely rare (but still just possible) to get a value below about 75 or above about 225.

For the sake of completeness, we have shown the theoretical form of the underlying gaussian curve as a full line in the figure, and indicated intervals equal to one standard deviation (σ). We will explain this further in the next section. For the moment it is sufficient to note the general shape of the curve; you may also like to try (and perhaps modify) the program for yourself.

Gaussian and uniform amplitude distributions are not the only types met in practice, but they are probably the most common. The gaussian case, in particular, has received a great deal of theoretical attention over the years and its properties are well known. As we shall see, it crops up regularly in DSP theory and practice.

4.2.2 Mean, mean-square and variance

The amplitude distribution of a random sequence, expressed in terms of a probability mass function or probability distribution function, gives us a complete statistical description of its amplitude characteristics. However, in many practical situations we do not need all this information; it may well be sufficient to know just the mean value, and the average size of fluctuations about the mean.

The *mean* of a random, quantised, digital sequence is defined as

$$m = E\{x[n]\} = \sum_{-\infty}^{\infty} x_n p_{x_n} \tag{4.4}$$

where E denotes mathematical expectation. Thus the mean is found by multiplying each allowed value of the sequence by the probability with which it occurs, followed by summation. It is the same as the *average* value of the sequence, and in electronic engineering is also widely referred to as the *dc value*.

The mean has several simple, and useful, properties. If each value of a sequence is multiplied by a constant, then its mean is multiplied by the same constant. Also, if we add together two or more random sequences to form a new sequence, then the mean of their sum equals the sum of their means. Note, however, that the mean of the *product* of two random variables is not, in general, equal to the product of their means (In situations where this does apply, the variables are said to be *linearly independent*, or *uncorrelated*. We will develop the very important topic of correlation in later sections.)

Another useful measure is the *mean-square*. In electrical terminology this is often referred to as the *average power* (from the notion that the mean-square value of a voltage or current waveform, associated with a 1 ohm resistor, gives its average power dissipation in watts). The mean-square of a digital sequence is defined as follows:

$$E\{x[n]^2\} = \sum_{-\infty}^{\infty} x_n{}^2 p_{x_n} \qquad (4.5)$$

Thus we form the square of each sequence value, multiply by the relevant probability, and sum over all possible values.

The third important measure to be considered is the *variance*, which refers to fluctuations around the mean, and is given the symbol σ^2. Thus

$$\sigma^2 = E\{(x[n] - m)^2\} \qquad (4.6)$$

The variance is therefore similar to the mean-square, but with the mean removed. Also, since the mean of a sum equals the sum of the means, it may easily be shown that

$$\text{variance} = \text{mean-square} - (\text{mean})^2 \qquad (4.7)$$

Equation (4.7) has a direct counterpart in electrical terms. Since the mean-square is equivalent to the total average power of a random variable, and the square of the mean represents the power in its dc component, it follows that the variance is a measure of the average power in all its other frequency components. We may therefore think of the variance as a measure of *fluctuation power* or *ac power*.

The square root of the variance is called the *standard deviation* (σ). It is an average measure of fluctuation amplitude about the mean. We have previously marked intervals equal to σ on the gaussian curve in part (b) of figure 4.3. Note that a gaussian sequence spends most of its time within about 2 standard deviations of the mean; the chance of finding it beyond about 4 standard deviations of the mean is extremely small.

You may find it helpful if we compute the values of mean, mean-square and variance for a familiar digital sequence – say that produced by a die-tossing experiment, in which we generate a set of integer numbers between 1 and 6. We have shown the relevant probability mass function in part (b) of figure 4.2. Using equations (4.4), (4.5) and (4.6) we obtain:

$$\text{mean} = 1(1/6) + 2(1/6) + 3(1/6) + 4(1/6) + 5(1/6) + 6(1/6)$$
$$= 21/6 = 3.5 \tag{4.8}$$

$$\text{mean-square} = 1^2(1/6) + 2^2(1/6) + \ldots 6^2(1/6) = 15.16667 \tag{4.9}$$

$$\text{variance} = (1 - 3.5)^2 (1/6) + (2 - 3.5)^2 (1/6) + \ldots$$
$$+ (6 - 3.5)^2 (1/6) = 2.91667 \tag{4.10}$$

You may like to check that the relationship between the three measures specified by equation (4.7) holds good in this case.

We noted previously that if two or more random processes are superposed to form a new process, then their means are additive. This also applies to their variances (but *not* their mean-square values), provided the individual random processes are statistically independent (uncorrelated). In electrical terms, this is equivalent to saying that the ac or fluctuation power of independent, superposed, random processes is additive.

The additive quality of variances can be demonstrated by an example. Suppose we form a random sequence by repeatedly tossing two dice, adding their scores to give an integer total between 2 and 12. The probability mass function for an individual die has already been shown in part (b) of figure 4.2. By considering all possible outcomes when two dice are tossed together, it is straightforward to show that the probability mass function is now as shown in figure 4.4. As we might expect, a total score of 2 or 12 is much less likely than one towards the centre of the range.

Using equations (4.4), (4.5) and (4.7) we obtain the following values for the mean, mean-square and variance of the new sequence:

$$\text{mean} = 7.0; \quad \text{mean-square} = 54.8333; \quad \text{variance} = 5.8333$$

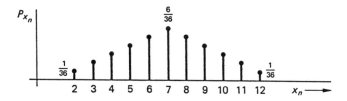

Figure 4.4 Probability mass function for the total score obtained with two dice

Comparing with equations (4.8)–(4.10), we see that the mean is twice that of the sequence obtained by tossing a single die; and so is the variance (even though the detailed form of the probability mass function is quite different in the two cases). Mean and variance are therefore additive; but the mean-square is not.

We have illustrated this section with die-tossing sequences because of their familiarity and conveniently small number of possible values. However the ideas we have developed apply equally well to a wide range of quantised digital sequences, representing both signals and noise.

4.2.3 Ensemble averages and time averages

In our discussions in this chapter so far, we have implied that the probabilities associated with the various discrete values of a random digital sequence are known in advance, or can be calculated. Furthermore, we have used these probabilities to infer such measures as the mean and variance of the values of the sequence. This raises a number of issues which need explanation and justification. In particular, we should clarify the distinction between what are known as *ensemble averages* and *time averages*.

Formally, a random or *stochastic* digital process is one giving rise to an infinite set of random variables, of which a particular sample sequence $x[n]$, $-\infty < n < \infty$, is merely one realisation. The set of all sequences which could be generated by the process is known as an infinite ensemble, and it is this to which the probability functions and expected values defined by equations (4.4)–(4.6) strictly refer. Such measures are therefore known as ensemble averages.

However in practical DSP we generally wish to deal with individual sequences, rather than ensembles. Each sample represents a single value of one of the variables described by the underlying stochastic process. We must therefore make a connection between ensemble properties and those of an individual sequence existing over a period of time.

The way forward is in terms of time averages. Thus we define such measures as the time-averaged mean and variance of an individual sequence:

$$m_x = \langle x[n] \rangle = \lim_{N \to \infty} \frac{1}{2N + 1} \sum_{n=-N}^{N} x[n] \qquad (4.11)$$

and

$$\sigma^2 = \langle (x[n] - m_x)^2 \rangle = \lim_{N \to \infty} \frac{1}{2N + 1} \sum_{n=-N}^{N} (x[n] - m_x)^2 \qquad (4.12)$$

It turns out that, under certain conditions, such time averages may indeed be used in place of ensemble averages.

The first condition is that the limits used in equations (4.11) and (4.12) only exist if the sequence $x[n]$ has a finite mean value and is *stationary*. A process is said to be stationary *in the strict sense* if all its statistics are independent of time origin. However in the case of linear DSP we can accept the less stringent condition of *wide-sense* stationarity. This requires only that the mean, and the correlation functions to be met in later sections, are independent of time origin. The practical reason for requiring stationarity is straightforward: if we are going to estimate measures such as the mean and variance of a sequence from its sample values, it is intuitively clear that the underlying statistics of the sequence must not change as time progresses.

Given wide-sense stationarity, we also require that the digital sequences we are dealing with obey the *ergodic hypothesis*. An ergodic process is indeed defined as one in which time averages equal ensemble expected averages. Although simply stated, ergodicity may be very difficult to prove. If you are interested in the theoretical background, you will find it explored in reference 18 in the Bibliography at the end of this book.

Fortunately the above conditions are met in a wide range of theoretical and practical problems encountered in linear DSP. In simple cases such as die-tossing, which we have used to illustrate previous sections, the equivalence of ensemble averages and time averages seems intuitively obvious. For example, if we put a large number of dice in a pot, and shake them all at once, we get an ensemble of individual scores. If we take a single die, and toss it many times, we get a sequence of scores. Provided all the dice are fair, and the fairness of the single die does not vary with repeated throws, common sense suggests that ensemble-averaged and time-averaged statistics must be the same.

There is one more important issue to be considered. The infinite limits used in equations (4.11) and (4.12) cannot be realised in practice, because we are always forced (by time, patience, or lack of computer storage!) to deal with sequences of finite duration. All we can do is *estimate* time averages for a *finite* sequence, and assume that our estimates are reasonable approximations to the underlying values.

Of course, this raises the question of the quality of estimates. How do we know that an estimate based on a finite sequence is reasonably accurate? The usual approach to this question relies on two ideas – the *bias* of an estimate, and its *variance*. An estimate is said to be *unbiased* if its expected value is the same as the true, underlying one. Naturally, we wish to make unbiased estimates whenever possible. Then, over a large number of individual trials, we may be sure that the average value of our estimates tends towards the true value we are seeking. Ideally, we should also like the variance to be as small as possible. This implies that estimates will tend to cluster around the true value, with the minimum of statistical variability. Finally, we note that an estimation algorithm is referred to as *consistent* if the bias and variance both tend asymptotically to zero as the sequence length on which they are based tends to infinity.

Analysis of the bias and variance of estimates is a complicated matter which is covered in more advanced books on DSP (for example, reference 5 in the Bibliography at the end of this book). Although we cannot go into theoretical detail here, it may be helpful to end this section by illustrating some of the above points with a computer program.

We have previously emphasised the importance of the gaussian distribution, pointing out that gaussian random sequences (and especially gaussian noise) often arise in practical DSP. Fortunately, it turns out that unbiassed and consistent estimates of such sequences are readily obtained. Our program, listed as Computer Program 8 in appendix A, starts by generating a gaussian sequence of 320 samples values. These may be thought of as a portion of an infinite sequence with zero mean value and unit variance. (A standard technique is employed here: we subtract 0.5 from each output of a random number generator to give a value between -0.5 and $+0.5$; twelve such values are then added to produce a new random number; and the process is repeated many times to give an (approximately) gaussian sequence. The variance of the initial random numbers is $1/12$, so that of the final sequence must be unity.) Our finite-length sequence is plotted in part (a) of figure 4.5.

Parts (b) and (c) of the figure show a series of estimates for mean and variance respectively. Each estimate is based on the 20 values of the sequence immediately preceding it. For example, the mean is estimated by adding together 20 successive sequence values, and dividing by 20. It is a well-known theoretical result that estimates formed in this way are unbiased and consistent in the case of a gaussian variable. The expected estimate of the mean is therefore zero, and of the variance unity. However, our individual results are quite variable. We could of course reduce the variability by using more sequence values in forming each estimate. There is always a trade-off between estimation time and the reliability of the result.

This last point suggests an alternative approach illustrated in parts (d) and (e) of the figure. Rather than divide the sequence up into independent blocks and form estimates for each in turn, we can compute a *running mean* and *running variance*. This is done by continuously updating our estimates as each new sequence value comes in; none of the data is discarded or forgotten. Note that, at the start of the exercise, we have very few data values to work with, and the estimates are very variable. But as we move towards the right of the figure, they tend more and more convincingly towards the underlying, expected values. Clearly, a longer sequence would yield still more reliable results.

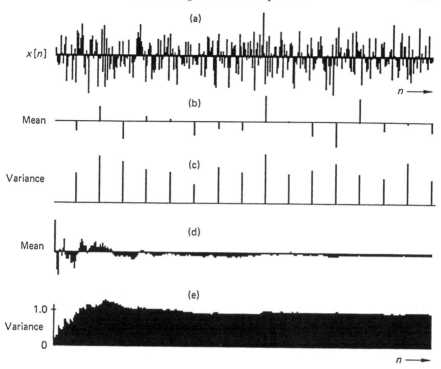

Figure 4.5   Computed estimates of mean and variance for a gaussian random sequence

You may like to try the program, running it several times to get a better idea of the chance variations that occur. A final point to make is that the estimates of variance are only unbiased because we are using the *true* mean (zero) to compute them. If we were to use the *estimated* mean in each case, they would contain bias – although to a diminishing extent as the sequence length increased.

4.2.4   Autocorrelation

At the start of section 4.2.2 we noted that the amplitude distribution of a random sequence gives a complete statistical description of its amplitude fluctuations. This is true as far as it goes; but it is important to realise that such a distribution is only a *first-order* measure. That is, it tells us about the probability of finding an individual sample value at various levels – but nothing about whether successive sample values are related to one another.

We can illustrate with two examples. If we toss a fair die, or a coin, we expect successive throws to be independent of one another. Knowledge of previous results does not help us to predict the next one. In such a situation the amplitude distribution (expressed as a probability mass or probability distribution function) completely defines the statistics of the process. However the filtered random sequence previously shown in part (b) of figure 4.1 is rather different. Here, groups of samples having similar values tend to cluster together. Knowledge of the sequence's recent history would obviously be a help in predicting the next value. In other words the sequence has a time-domain *structure* – and it is this structure which we must be able to characterise. The most widely used measure for this purpose is the *autocorrelation function*.

You probably recall that first-order measures such as the mean and variance are formally defined in terms of probability functions and ensemble averages. Then, assuming stationarity and ergodicity, we extend the definitions to encompass time averages taken over a single digital sequence. The same approach is valid with correlation functions. Therefore, rather than go over similar ground again, we will straight away define the autocorrelation function, and its close cousin the *autocovariance function*, in terms of time averages:

Autocorrelation

$$\phi_{xx}[m] = \langle x[n]\, x[n+m] \rangle$$

$$= \lim_{N \to \infty} \frac{1}{2N+1} \sum_{n=-N}^{N} x[n]\, x[n+m] \qquad (4.13)$$

Autocovariance

$$\gamma_{xx}[m] = \langle (x[n] - m_x)(x[n+m] - m_x) \rangle$$

$$= \lim_{N \to \infty} \frac{1}{2N+1} \sum_{n=-N}^{N} (x[n] - m_x)(x[n+m] - m_x) \qquad (4.14)$$

Equation (4.13) shows that the autocorrelation function (ACF) is the average product of the sequence $x[n]$ with a time-shifted version of itself. It is therefore a *second-order* measure, and is a function of the imposed time shift m. Provided $x[n]$ is stationary, the ACF is independent of time origin. Autocorrelation is a valuable measure of the statistical dependence between values of $x[n]$ at different times, and summarises its time-domain structure.

The autocovariance function defined by equation (4.14) is similar to the ACF, except that the mean is removed. In the case of a random variable having zero mean, the autocorrelation and autocovariance functions are identical. In the more general case we may write

$$\gamma_{xx}[m] = \phi_{xx}[m] - m_x^2 \qquad (4.15)$$

As with the first-order measures discussed in previous sections, when computing the ACF or autocovariance we must settle for estimates based on finite sequence lengths. Such estimates always possess statistical variability, and only tend towards the true, underlying functions as the sequence length tends to infinity.

A major advantage of autocorrelating a random sequence is that in most cases the resulting function tends to die away for large values (both positive and negative) of the time-shift variable m. This means that a sequence of long (and even infinitely long) duration can be characterised by a statistical function of reasonable length. Not only is this compactness valuable in its own right, but – as we shall see later – it has important implications for estimating the spectral characteristics of the sequence.

Let us now use a computer to illustrate some of the main features of autocorrelation and autocovariance functions. Figure 4.6 shows, on the left-hand side, portions of five different sequences and, on the right, their computed autocorrelation functions. Although we have plotted only 150 values of each sequence, the ACFs were estimated using 1001 values ($N = 500$ in equation (4.13)) in order to give reasonably reliable estimates. Also, we have computed each ACF over the restricted range $-50 \leq m \leq 50$. This is sufficient to establish its general form, without getting involved in too much computation.

Parts (a) and (b) of the figure show two deterministic sequences: a sinusoid; and a cosinusoid plus a dc level. You may find these choices rather surprising, because the whole emphasis of our discussion is on random functions. The reason is that the ACFs of sines and cosines are quite easy to visualise and relate to equation (4.13). When we have done this, we can tackle some more complicated examples with confidence.

What happens when we autocorrelate the sinusoid shown in part (a)? As equation (4.13) makes clear, we multiply a long portion of the sequence by a shifted version of itself, and average the result. The process is then repeated for different values of the shift parameter m. It is clear that when the shift is zero, positive peaks of the sinusoid align with positive peaks, and negative peaks with negative peaks, giving a large positive product. Hence we expect the ACF to be large and positive for $m = 0$.

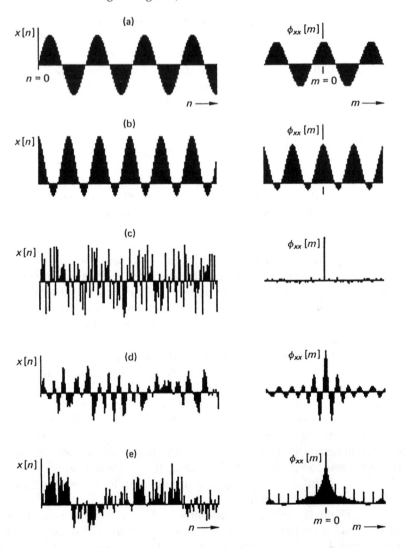

Figure 4.6 Five digital sequences and their estimated autocorrelation functions (*abscissae: 150 and 100 samples*)

As we start to introduce time shift ('sliding' one version of the sequence beneath the other, cross-multiplying and summing), the positive and negative peaks begin to lose their alignment. By the time all positive peaks are aligned with negative ones, and vice-versa, the ACF will have a large negative value. As the sliding process continues, it is clear that the ACF will trace out a repetitive function, whose period in the time-shift variable m equals the period of the sequence itself in the time variable n.

We conclude that a repetitive sequence $x[n]$ has an ACF which is also repetitive, with the same period. In the special case of a sinusoidal sequence, it turns out that the ACF takes a cosinusoidal form. And since the mean value of the sequence is zero in this case, the ACF is the same as the autocovariance function.

Part (b) of the figure shows a cosine sequence plus a dc level. As before, the ACF is periodic with a peak value at $m = 0$. Note that the finite mean value is also represented. This illustrates the fact that an ACF contains all the frequency components present in the sequence itself. And it may be shown (see, for example, reference 16 in the Bibliography at the end of this book) that each component has an amplitude proportional to the *square* of that in the original sequence – in other words, an amplitude which represents the component's *average power*.

We can develop this point a little further by noting that the central value of an ACF equals the mean square value of the sequence, and is therefore a measure of its total power. Thus, setting $m = 0$ in equation (4.13) we obtain:

$$\phi_{xx}[0] = \langle (x[n])^2 \rangle \qquad (4.16)$$

The central value is always a maximum value. It may be equalled at other values of time shift, but it can never be exceeded.

Similarly, by putting $m = 0$ in equation (4.14), we see that the central value of an autocovariance function equals the *variance* of the corresponding sequence – equivalent to its ac power.

We should be a little careful using the word 'power', because the idea of average power really only applies to signals which continue for ever. In the case of practical, time-limited signals we should talk *either* about power averaged over their actual duration, *or* about their total energy.

We next consider ACF estimates for three random functions. Part (c) of figure 4.6 shows, on the left, a sequence of uniformly distributed random numbers in the range -1 to $+1$. Successive values may be assumed independent. When such a sequence is autocorrelated, we get a large central peak at $m = 0$, with zero values to either side (actually, the estimate shows small residues to either side – the typical effect of working with a finite-length sequence). We may visualise this result as follows. At zero time shift, positive and negative values align with themselves, giving a large positive product. But at any other value of time shift, a given sample is just as likely to align with one of opposite sign, so the cross-product averages out to zero. In other words there is no correlation between adjacent sample values; the sequence is entirely random.

For reasons which will become clear later, a sequence with this type of ACF is often called *white noise*. Note that the term refers to the form of the

ACF (with its isolated central spike), *not* to the amplitude distribution of the sequence. For example, a gaussian sequence and a uniformly-distributed sequence can both be 'white' – provided successive sample values are truly independent.

Part (d) of the figure shows a similar sequence after bandpass filtering. The ACF now spreads considerably to either side of $m = 0$, reflecting correlation between adjacent sample values. In this example there is quite a strong correlation up to time shifts of about $m = \pm 10$. If we processed the sequence with a filter of narrower bandwidth, the ACF would spread even further; but it would eventually decay towards zero.

In part (e) we have processed white noise with a low-pass filter, and then added a repetitive impulse train with a period of 8 sampling intervals. You may or may not feel that you can detect the impulse train in the sequence itself; but autocorrelation brings it out clearly. Note how the filtered noise only contributes to the ACF around $m = 0$, whereas the pulse train, being strictly repetitive, contributes over the complete range of time shift. This suggests an important practical application for autocorrelation – the detection of a repetitive signal in the presence of unwanted noise.

We hope you now have some insight into the process of autocorrelation, and the forms of ACF likely to be met in practice. You have probably noticed that an ACF is always an even function of time shift. Intuitively, this is because the result of cross-multiplication and summation is independent of the direction of shift. It follows that we could save on computation by estimting only 'one half' of the function. There are also important implications for the spectral properties of random sequences which we explore in the next section.

4.2.5 Power spectrum

Every time-domain function has a counterpart in the frequency domain. In the case of an autocorrelation function (ACF), which is a function of the time-shift variable m, the counterpart is called a *power spectral density* or, more simply, a *power spectrum*. It indicates how the sequence's power or energy is distributed in the frequency domain, and is a widely-used measure of random sequences.

Formally, the ACF and power spectrum of a digital sequence are related as a Fourier Transform pair (see section 1.4.2). Thus the power spectrum is defined as

$$P_{xx}(\Omega) = \sum_{m=-\infty}^{\infty} \phi_{xx}[m] \exp(-j\Omega m) \tag{4.17}$$

An alternative definition, found in some texts, specifies the autocovariance function instead of the ACF. This avoids problems which arise when the underlying sequence has a non-zero mean value (giving a rather awkward zero-frequency impulse in the power spectrum). In the following discussion we will assume zero-mean sequences for which the autocorrelation and autocovariance functions are identical.

The inverse transform gives the ACF in terms of the power spectrum:

$$\phi_{xx}[m] = \frac{1}{2\pi} \int_{2\pi} P_{xx}(\Omega) \exp(j\Omega m) \, d\Omega \tag{4.18}$$

Note also that by putting $m = 0$ we obtain

$$\phi_{xx}[0] = \frac{1}{2\pi} \int_{2\pi} P_{xx}(\Omega) \, d\Omega \tag{4.19}$$

Now $\phi_{xx}[0]$ represents the sequence's total power (see equation (4.16)). We see that it is equal to $1/2\pi$ times the area under the power spectrum curve over any 2π interval.

Intuitively, there are two main reasons why the function $P_{xx}(\Omega)$ relates to the power distribution of a sequence. Firstly, in forming an ACF we multiply the sequence by a shifted version of itself, giving rise to a second-order, 'amplitude-squared' measure having dimensions of power or energy. And secondly, as we pointed out in the previous section, an ACF is always an even function of time shift. It follows that its spectral equivalent must be a real function of Ω, with no information about the relative phases of the various frequency components present. A measure which relates to power, rather than amplitude and phase, meets this criterion.

The spectral representation of digital signals in terms of Fourier and *z*-Transforms has previously been described in chapter 1. One of the conditions for such a transform to exist is that the sequence concerned should have *finite energy* – or it must be possible to multiply by an exponential so that the product has finite energy. This can lead to difficulties with some important types of sequences, including random noise, which in theory continue for ever and therefore possess *infinite energy*. However, the ACF offers a way forward. As we have seen in figure 4.6, the ACF of a zero-mean random sequence generally decays towards zero to either side of $m = 0$, and may therefore be represented as a finite-energy sequence – for which the Fourier and *z*-Transforms do exist. The ACF is therefore not only a useful function in its own right; it also provides us with a useful route to the spectral representation of a random, infinite-energy sequence.

We previously discussed the practical difficulties which arise in computing a sequence's ACF. Basically, the problem is that we can only work with a finite portion of the sequence, and estimate the ACF for a limited set of time-shift, or *lag*, values. If you refer back to parts (c), (d), and (e) of figure 4.6, you will see that not only are the computed ACFs subject to random variability, but they are also restricted to lag values in the range ±50. In each case we end up with an estimate of the true, underlying function.

What effect does the use of an *estimated* ACF have on a power spectrum obtained using equation (4.17)? Firstly, if we assume the ACF to be zero outside the estimated range, we are effectively truncating it with a rectangular window. This tends to produce substantial sidelobes in the power spectrum as a result of the Gibbs' phenomenon (see section 2.1.3). It is therefore common practice to multiply the estimated ACF by a tapered window function such as a Bartlett (triangular) or Hamming window before Fourier Transformation. This reduces sidelobes, and also has the desirable effect of improving the statistical reliability of the resulting power spectrum – a particular advantage when the ACF estimate is based on a short sequence, with maximum lag values comparable with the length of the sequence itself. However, as always, there is a price to be paid: such a window has a pronounced smoothing effect, which reduces spectral resolution.

Some of these points are illustrated by figure 4.7, which shows estimated ACFs and power spectra for a bandpass-filtered noise sequence. In part (a)

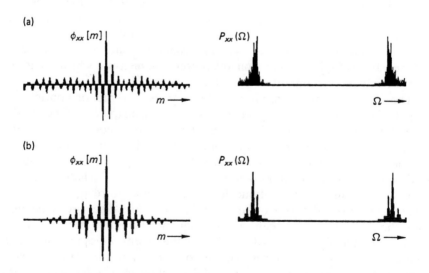

Figure 4.7   Autocorrelation and power spectral estimates for a bandpass-filtered noise sequence (*abscissae: 256 samples*)

the ACF has been formed by cross-multiplying 1024 values of an infinite sequence, for lag values in the range $-128 \leq m \leq 128$. We may expect the resulting ACF to be quite reliable; but, of course, we have had to perform a lot of computation (including some $1024 \times 256 = 262\ 144$ multiplications). Using the FFT listed as Computer Program 6 in appendix A, we obtain the power spectrum estimate on the right-hand side of the figure. Although it contains some chance variations, we may be confident about its overall shape – including the clear peak around $\Omega = \pi/5$ (corresponding to frequency components with about 10 samples per period, as indicated by the ACF). In fact, a smooth curve drawn through the various frequency-domain samples would, in this case, get close to the underlying power spectrum (which is a continuous function of Ω).

However in many cases we do not have so much data to work with, or we cannot afford so much computation. Part (b) of the figure shows another estimated ACF, this time based on a finite portion of the sequence with just 128 sample values. Assuming the sequence is zero outside the observed interval, we are effectively multiplying the infinite sequence by a rectangular window. Then, sliding the time-limited sequence over itself to estimate the ACF, we get less and less overlap as the lag increases. As we approach lags of $m = \pm 128$, the ACF values become very unreliable. It is therefore only sensible to taper the result, reducing the importance attached to values in the 'tails'. In the example shown we have tapered with a triangular (Bartlett) window.

The power spectrum estimate on the right-hand side was obtained by Fourier Transformation of the windowed ACF, again using a 256-point FFT. It has the same general form as that in part (a); but there is a loss of detail, and a tendency for spurious peaks and troughs to occur. Although these results should be taken as illustrative rather than definitive, they emphasise the problem of obtaining reliable power spectral estimates from limited data sequences. Of course, the problem becomes worse if – as quite often happens – we have to work with even shorter sequences and fewer lag values.

In spite of such reservations, the power spectra of random sequences are widely estimated using the above approach. Because it works via the ACF, it is often referred to as the *indirect method*.

When dealing with a time-limited sequence $x[n]$, an alternative approach to power spectrum estimation, often called the *direct method*, is possible. We first compute the Fourier Transform of $x[n]$ to give the normal type of spectrum $X(\Omega)$. Then, discarding phase information, we find the squared-magnitude and divide by the sequence length. This gives the following power spectrum estimate:

$$P'_{xx}(\Omega) = \frac{1}{N} \left| X(\Omega) \right|^2 = \frac{1}{N} \left| \sum_{n=0}^{N-1} x[n] \exp(-j\Omega n) \right|^2 \qquad (4.20)$$

Such an estimate is generally referred to as a *periodogram*. Of course, the method implies that we have knowledge of the individual sample values of the random sequence – as opposed to the time-averaged statistics represented by its ACF. (Also, an ACF may sometimes be inferred theoretically, rather than by computations based on an actual sequence. A periodogram can only use the latter approach.)

The periodogram approach turns out to be the same as that derived by the indirect method, provided the following *biased* estimate of the ACF is used in equation (4.17):

$$\phi'_{xx}[m] = \frac{1}{N} \sum_{n=0}^{N-|m|-1} x[n] \, x[n + m] \qquad (4.21)$$

Note that this differs from our previous ACF estimates in that the multiplying factor in front of the summation is now $1/N$, even though the number of cross-products we form $(n - |m|)$ diminishes as the lag value m increases. Thus we are not now forming the average cross-product, but linearly reducing the attention paid to values in the 'tails'. This is exactly what we did when applying a Bartlett window to the ACF in part (b) of figure 4.7. We conclude that a periodogram estimate achieves the same result as taking the Fourier Transform of an ACF weighted by a Bartlett window.

Figure 4.8 illustrates a periodogram for the bandpass-filtered random sequence already used in figure 4.7. It was obtained by zero-filling the 128-point sequence shown on the left up to 256 values, then using a 256-point FFT and computing squared magnitudes. This allows a more direct comparison with part (b) of figure 4.7. Note the similar tendency for spurious peaks and troughs, and the loss of spectral resolution.

Both indirect and direct approaches to power spectrum estimation have been widely used in practice, mainly because of the speed and convenience of the FFT. Unfortunately, however, the resulting estimates are generally inconsistent, in the sense that their variance fails to approach zero as the sequence length N increases. In the case of a periodogram, although the spectral resolution improves with increasing N, chance fluctuations about the true spectral values do not tend to zero. They merely become more

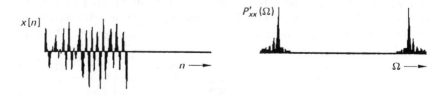

Figure 4.8   A time-limited sequence and its periodogram

rapid. The problem can be reduced by using some form of averaging or smoothing in the frequency domain – a matter much more fully discussed in, for example, reference 5 in the Bibliography at the end of this book.

To conclude this section, we should emphasise that the above methods of spectral estimation do not always give acceptable spectral resolution. Various more modern approaches have been developed, in which the random sequence is modelled as the output of an LTI system or processor driven by white noise. By making reasonable assumptions about the structure and order of the system it is often possible, in effect, to extrapolate the ACF outside the observation interval. Such model-based methods include the so-called *moving average, autoregressive moving average* and *maximum entropy* techniques (see reference 12 in the Bibliography given at the end of this book).

4.2.6 Cross-correlation

We have seen how autocorrelation may be used to characterise a sequence's time-domain structure. Cross-correlation is an essentially similar process; but instead of comparing a sequence with a shifted version of itself, it compares two different sequences. The *cross-correlation function (CCF)* of sequences $x[n]$ and $y[n]$, and its close cousin the *cross-covariance function*, may be defined in terms of time averages:

Cross-correlation

$$\phi_{xy}[m] = \langle x[n]\, y[n + m] \rangle$$

$$= \lim_{N \to \infty} \frac{1}{2N + 1} \sum_{n=-N}^{N} x[n]\, y[n + m] \tag{4.22}$$

Cross-covariance

$$\gamma_{xy}[m] = \langle (x[n] - m_x)(y[n + m] - m_y) \rangle$$

$$= \lim_{N \to \infty} \frac{1}{2N + 1} \sum_{n=-N}^{N} (x[n] - m_x)(y[n + m] - m_y) \tag{4.23}$$

Both these functions are second-order measures. The CCF provides a statistical comparison of two sequences as a function of the time shift between them. Cross-covariance is similar, except that the mean values of the two sequences are removed.

Just as the form of an ACF reflects the various frequency components in the underlying sequence, so that of a CCF reflects components *held in common* between $x[n]$ and $y[n]$. However whereas an ACF, being an even function, retains no phase information, a CCF holds information about the relative phases of shared frequency components. It follows that a CCF is not generally an even function of the time-shift parameter m.

We can demonstrate some of these ideas with the help of a computer. Part (a) of figure 4.9 shows portions of two random sequences $x[n]$ and $y[n]$, which are both strong in frequencies having about 12 samples per period. In addition, $y[n]$ contains substantial high-frequency energy at around 2 samples per period. Their CCF, shown in part (b), has been estimated using equation (4.22), but with $N = 500$, and values of m between 0 and 99. We have of course obtained only a portion of the total function. Nevertheless, it is clear that the CCF estimate reflects only shared frequencies in $x[n]$ and $y[n]$. There is no sign of the high-frequency energy contained in $y[n]$.

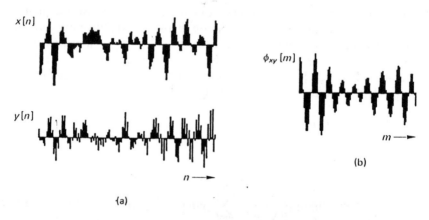

(a)

(b)

Figure 4.9   Estimating a cross-correlation function

The fine detail of such a CCF can be hard to interpret, and when our main interest is in shared frequencies, or frequency ranges, it is generally better to use an equivalent spectral description (to be covered in the next section). However from a practical point of view there is one major type of situation in which the CCF can be particularly revealing – namely when there are *timing differences* between the two sequences being compared. To take a simple case, suppose that $x[n]$ and $y[n]$ are identical white noise sequences which differ only in their time origin. Their CCF is then expected to be zero for all values of m, except the one which exactly offsets, or cancels, the timing difference.

A rather more challenging example is illustrated in figure 4.10. Part (a) shows portions of two sequences $x[n]$ and $y[n]$, which we may suspect are

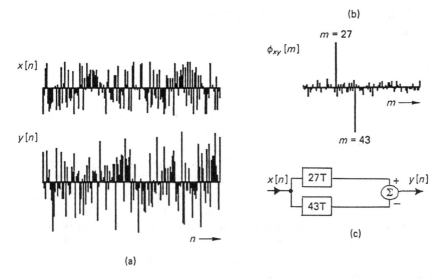

Figure 4.10 Using cross-correlation to reveal timing differences between two random sequences

related in some way. We compute an estimate of their CCF, shown in part (b) of the figure (this was found in exactly the same way as that of part (b) of figure 4.9). The result suggests very little correlation between the sequences, except for two particular lag values ($m = 27$ and $m = 43$). It implies that $y[n]$ could well have arisen by the superposition of two versions of $x[n]$ – one delayed by 27 sampling intervals; the other delayed by 43 sampling intervals, and inverted. This is shown by part (c) of the figure. Although it is not the only possible explanation for the form of the CCF, it is a very plausible one. Note how hard it is to detect any such relationship in the sequences themselves.

The figure suggests the possibility of using cross-correlation to infer the properties of an LTI processor or system. This very important idea has found widespread practical application and will be discussed further in section 5.3.

Of course, in all such cases we must take care to estimate the CCF over a suitable, and sufficient, range of time-delay values to avoid missing essential features. This is largely a matter of judgement and experience, although we sometimes have additional *a priori* information which helps us make a sensible choice.

A final point to make about cross-correlation is that it reveals only *linear* relationships between the two sequences being compared. Put at its simplest, this means that if $y[n]$ could have been produced by passing $x[n]$ through an LTI processor (or vice versa), then their CCF may be used to define the relationship. But if, for example, $y[n]$ is a squared version of

$x[n]$, the CCF will generally give a false indication – and may even suggest no relationship at all.

4.2.7 Cross-spectrum

The frequency-domain counterpart of a cross-correlation function (CCF) relating two sequences $x[n]$ and $y[n]$ is known as a *cross-spectral density*, or simply as a *cross-spectrum*. It gives us valuable information about frequencies held in common between $x[n]$ and $y[n]$. Thus if $x[n]$ has a component $A_1 \sin(n\Omega_1 + \theta)$ and $y[n]$ has a component $A_2 \sin(n\Omega_1 + \psi)$, their cross-spectrum will have magnitude $A_1 A_2/2$ and phase $(\theta - \psi)$ at frequency Ω. This shows that a shared component is represented in proportion to the *product* of the individual amplitudes, and with a phase equal to the *difference* between the individual phases. Since a cross-spectrum holds phase information, it is generally a complex function of Ω. In this respect it differs from the power spectrum of an individual sequence, which is always real.

If two sequences $x[n]$ and $y[n]$ have no shared frequencies, or frequency ranges, their cross-spectrum (like their CCF) is zero. They are said to be *linearly independent*, or *orthogonal*. This implies that $y[n]$ could not be formed by passing $x[n]$ through a linear processor – or vice versa.

Formally, the cross-spectrum $P_{xy}(\Omega)$ and CCF are related as a Fourier Transform pair. Thus

$$P_{xy}(\Omega) = \sum_{m=-\infty}^{\infty} \phi_{xy}[m] \exp(-j\Omega m) \tag{4.24}$$

and

$$\phi_{xy}[m] = \frac{1}{2\pi} \int_{2\pi} P_{xy}(\Omega) \exp(j\Omega m) \, d\Omega \tag{4.25}$$

When $x[n]$ and $y[n]$ both have non-zero mean values, the above definition of $P_{xy}(\Omega)$ results in a rather awkward frequency-domain impulse at $\Omega = 0$. For this reason, the cross-spectrum is sometimes defined as the Fourier Transform of the cross-covariance (see equation (4.23)) rather than the CCF. In the following discussion we will assume sequences with zero mean values, for which the CCF and cross-covariance are identical.

In section 4.2.5 we described the practical difficulty of obtaining a reliable estimate for the power spectrum of a time-limited random sequence. Very similar problems apply to cross-spectrum estimation. Once again it is helpful to taper the time-domain function (in this case the CCF) with a suitable window function before transformation. Tapering with a Bartlett window is a popular choice, and is equivalent to forming the following biased CCF estimate, with a weighting which reduces linearly towards the 'tails':

$$\phi'_{xy}[m] = \frac{1}{N} \sum_{n=0}^{N-m-1} x[n]\, y[n+m], \quad 0 \leqslant m \leqslant N$$

$$= \frac{1}{N} \sum_{n=0}^{N+m-1} x[n]\, y[n+m], \quad 0 > m > -N \qquad (4.26)$$

Fourier Transformation produces an asymptotically unbiased estimate of the cross-spectrum:

$$P'_{xx}(\Omega) = \sum_{m=-(N-1)}^{N-1} \phi'_{xy}[m]\, \exp(-j\Omega m) \qquad (4.27)$$

Note that if $x[n] = y[n]$, this result is similar to the periodogram of a single sequence. As with the periodogram, it is unfortunately inconsistent, in that the variance does not tend to zero as the sequence lengths increase. Some form of averaging or smoothing is therefore normally used in the frequency domain to reduce variability, at the expense of spectral resolution.

Apart from its value as a measure of shared frequencies between two sequences, the cross-spectrum relating random input and output signals of an LTI processor can be used to infer the properties of the processor itself. We shall return to this important idea in section 5.3.

Problems

4.1. A random digital sequence takes on three distinct values, 1, 0 and −1, all with equal probability.

(a) Sketch its probability mass and probability distribution functions.

(b) Estimate its mean, mean-square and variance.

4.2. A die has been unfairly loaded to give the following probabilities associated with its six possible scores:

score	1	2	3	4	5	6
probability	0.1	0.15	0.15	0.15	0.15	0.3

(a) Sketch its probability mass and probability distribution functions.

(b) Estimate the mean, mean-square and variance of scores.

4.3. Explain clearly:

    (a) the distinction between ensemble averages and time averages
    (b) the meaning of the term 'unbiased estimate'
    (c) the distinction between autocorrelation and autocovariance functions.

4.4. Make careful sketches of the autocorrelation functions of the following:

    (a) the random digital sequence specified in problem **4.1**
    (b) the sequence obtained when a fair six-faced die is tossed repeatedly
    (c) the sequence obtained when the unfair die described in problem **4.2** is tossed repeatedly
    (d) the sequence illustrated in part (b) of figure 4.1 of the main text.

In all cases except (d), specify the central peak value of the ACF.

4.5. The ACF of a random digital signal is shown in figure P4.5. Find the signal's mean value, mean-square value and standard deviation.
    Over what time interval are signal fluctuations significantly correlated?

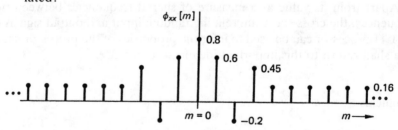

Figure P4.5

4.6. Find expressions for, and sketch, the power spectra corresponding to the ACFs in parts (a) and (b) of problem **4.4**.

4.7. The power spectrum of a random signal over the range $-\pi \leqslant \Omega \leqslant \pi$ is given by:

$$P_{xx}(\Omega) = 1, \quad -\pi/4 \leqslant \Omega \leqslant \pi/4$$

$$= 0, \quad \text{elsewhere}$$

(a) Find an expression for, and sketch, the signal's ACF.

(b) Find the signal's total average power.

4.8. Repeat problem **4.7** for a signal having the power spectrum:

$$P_{xx}(\Omega) = 1 + 0.5 \cos\Omega + 0.25 \cos2\Omega$$

4.9. Discuss the value of cross-correlation for quantifying the relationship between the two random sequences.

4.10. Long portions of two random digital signals are cross-correlated. The resulting function is found to have the following values:

$$\phi_{xy}[m] = 1, \quad m = 0, 3$$

$$= 2, \quad m = 1, 2$$

$$= 0, \quad \text{elsewhere}$$

Find an expression for the cross-spectrum.

5 Processing Random Sequences

5.1 Response of linear processors

In the previous chapter we saw how to characterise a random sequence in terms of such long-term average measures as the mean, variance, autocorrelation function (ACF) and power spectrum. An obvious question now arises: how are such measures modified by linear processing? This is a matter of the greatest importance for describing the passage of random signals or noise (or signals contaminated by noise) through a filter or processor. And, as we shall discover, the first- and second-order measures described in previous chapters have the advantage of being readily related to the effects of LTI processing.

The idea of digital convolution was developed back in section 1.3.2, where we showed how the impulse response $h[n]$ of a processor could be used to assess its response to any input signal $x[n]$. Figure 1.14 illustrated a graphical interpretation of convolution, in which a time-reversed version of $h[n]$ was laid beneath $x[n]$, followed by cross-multiplication and summation to yield a particular value of the output signal $y[n]$. The same process is valid for a random input sequence. Figure 5.1 shows a portion of such a sequence and, beneath it, a typical reversed impulse response. Cross-

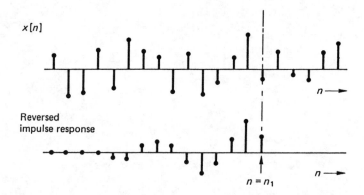

Figure 5.1

multiplication and summation gives the output sample value relevant to the instant $n = n_1$. By moving the reversed impulse response along step-by-step and repeating the process, we generate the complete output sequence according to the convolution sum (see also equation (1.17)):

$$y(n) = \sum_{k=-\infty}^{\infty} x[n - k] h[k] \tag{5.1}$$

Figure 5.1 makes clear that each random output value is a weighted sum of a set of random inputs, the weightings being given by the various impulse response terms. We must therefore expect some correlation between adjacent outputs (whether or not successive inputs are correlated), because the outputs are not formed independently of one another. This will happen with any processor possessing memory. Such insights are very helpful for visualising the effects of linear processing on random sequences.

Before getting down to detail, it is worth noting that a stationary input sequence applied to an LTI processor produces a stationary output. This implies that the various statistical measures we wish to use are independent of time origin at both input and output.

Figure 5.2 summarises the situation. A random input sequence forms the input to an LTI processor with impulse response $h[n]$ and frequency response $H(\Omega)$, producing an output sequence $y[n]$. Input and output are characterised by their mean, variance, ACF and power spectrum. Equation (5.1) deals with individual sample values and is not therefore of direct use as it stands. However we can modify it to cope with time-averaged measures. Thus the mean, or expected, value of the output sequence may be derived as follows:

$$m_y = E\{y[n]\} = \sum_{k=-\infty}^{\infty} E\{x[n - k]\} h[k]$$

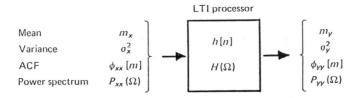

Figure 5.2   Signal statistics across an LTI processor

$$= m_x \sum_{k=-\infty}^{\infty} h[k] \tag{5.2}$$

This result uses the fact that the expectation of a sum equals the sum of the expectations. It shows that the mean of the output is given by the mean of the input multiplied by the sum of all impulse response terms – a simple and attractive result. Furthermore, in the frequency domain the mean (or dc) value of the output equals that of the input, multiplied by the zero-frequency (or dc) response of the processor. Thus

$$m_y = m_x H(0) \tag{5.3}$$

We will next tackle the relationship between input and output ACFs, returning to the question of variances later. Again using equation (5.1), the output ACF may be written as

$$\phi_{yy}[m] = E\{y[n]\, y[n+m]\} \tag{5.4}$$

$$= E\left\{ \sum_{k=-\infty}^{\infty} x[n-k]\, h[k] \sum_{r=-\infty}^{\infty} x[n+m-r]\, h[r] \right\}$$

$$= \sum_{k=-\infty}^{\infty} h[k] \sum_{r=-\infty}^{\infty} E\{x[n-k]\, x[n+m-r]\}\, h[r] \tag{5.5}$$

The expectation of this last expression equals the value of the input ACF relevant to the time shift $(m + k - r)$. Hence

$$\phi_{yy}[m] = \sum_{k=-\infty}^{\infty} h[k] \sum_{r=-\infty}^{\infty} \phi_{xx}[m+k-r]\, h[r] \tag{5.6}$$

It is now helpful to substitute q for $(r - k)$, giving

$$\phi_{yy}[m] = \sum_{k=-\infty}^{\infty} h[k] \sum_{q=-\infty}^{\infty} \phi_{xx}[m-q]\, h[k+q]$$

$$= \sum_{q=-\infty}^{\infty} \phi_{xx}[m-q] \sum_{k=-\infty}^{\infty} h[k]\, h[k+q] \tag{5.7}$$

If we write

$$j[m] = \sum_{k=-\infty}^{\infty} h[k]\, h[k+m] \tag{5.8}$$

we obtain

$$\phi_{yy}[m] = \sum_{q=-\infty}^{\infty} \phi_{xx}[m-q]\, j[q] \tag{5.9}$$

Note that $j[m]$ is the autocorrelation sequence of the impulse response $h[n]$. Hence this last equation tells us that the output ACF may be found by convolving the input ACF with the ACF of the processor's impulse response. It is a very important result.

Equation (5.9) also provides the key to the relationship between input and output variances. Putting $m = 0$ we obtain the peak central value of the output ACF:

$$\phi_{yy}[0] = \sum_{q=-\infty}^{\infty} \phi_{xx}[-q]\, j[q] \tag{5.10}$$

Since an ACF is always an even function of time-shift, we may also write

$$\phi_{yy}[0] = \sum_{m=-\infty}^{\infty} \phi_{xx}[m]\, j[m] \tag{5.11}$$

Now the output variance is given by the central value of the output covariance function $\gamma_{yy}[m]$ – a point already made in section 4.2.4. From equation (4.15) we obtain

$$\sigma_y^2 = \gamma_{yy}[0] = \phi_{yy}[0] - m_y^2 \tag{5.12}$$

Substitution using equations (5.2) and (5.11) yields

$$\sigma_y^2 = \sum_{m=-\infty}^{\infty} \phi_{xx}[m]\, j[m] - \left(m_x \sum_{n=-\infty}^{\infty} h[n] \right)^2 \tag{5.13}$$

We have now expressed the output variance in terms of the mean m_x and autocorrelation function $\phi_{xx}[m]$ of the input, and the impulse response $h[n]$ and autocorrelation sequence $j[m]$ of the processor.

The other measure we wish to consider is the output power spectrum. This can either be found as the Fourier Transform of the output ACF given by equation (5.9), or derived directly from the input power spectrum. The basic notion here is that the frequency response $H(\Omega)$ of a processor defines its effect, in amplitude and phase, on an input frequency Ω. Since power is proportional to amplitude-squared and involves no phase information, the equivalent 'power response' of the processor is $|H(\Omega)|^2$. Hence we may write directly:

$$P_{yy}(\Omega) = |H(\Omega)|^2 \, P_{xx}(\Omega) \tag{5.14}$$

You perhaps find the above results – and especially those involving correlation functions – a little hard to visualise. So we will now use a computer program to illustrate some of the key input–output relationships. Computer Program 9 in appendix A may be summarised as follows:

1. The impulse response values of the desired processor are first entered (up to 10 are allowed). The values listed in the appendix represent a simple bandpass function; they may, of course, be altered as required.
2. A gaussian noise sequence with zero mean and unit variance is generated. Although we could use this directly as input to the processor, it is more instructive to pass it first through a shaping filter (giving a more interesting input ACF), and add a finite mean. Here we use a simple 4-point shaping filter with low-pass properties, then add 1.0 to each sample value. We end up with a sequence $x[n]$ which is suitable for demonstration purposes. 320 values of $x[n]$ are plotted on the screen, as shown in part (a) of figure 5.3.
3. The ACF of $x[n]$, denoted by $\phi_{xx}[m]$, is now plotted (see part (c) of the figure). This is a theoretical result based on the form of the shaping filter's impulse response. Note that it includes a substantial dc pedestal, representing the mean value of $x[n]$.
4. The impulse response of the desired LTI processor, given as data at the start of the program, is used to calculate the following: its own ACF (represented by $j[m]$ in equation (5.8)); the mean value of the output (see equation (5.2)); and hence the output ACF (see equation 5.9)). The latter is also plotted on the screen – see part (d) of the figure – and represents the convolution of the input ACF with $j[m]$.
5. The actual output sample sequence is now found by convolving $x[n]$ and $h[n]$. 320 of its values are plotted in part (b) of the figure. Note that the bandpass properties of the LTI processor are clearly visible.

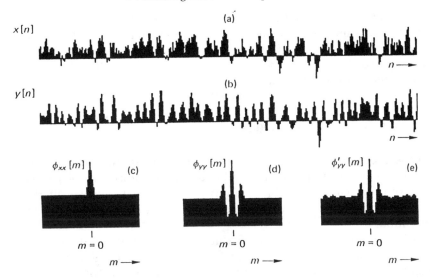

Figure 5.3 (a) Random input signal, and (b) random output of an LTI processor. Also shown are: (c) the input ACF; (d) the output ACF; and (e) a practical estimate of the output ACF based on 1000 samples of $y[n]$ (*abscissae: 320 and 83 samples*)

6. A practical estimate of the output ACF is now computed, for comparison with the predicted result in part (d) of the figure. The estimate is based on 1000 values of $y[n]$ and is built up on the screen as the computation proceeds (see part (e) of the figure). This may take several minutes if you are using a personal computer – but it is instructive to see the function developing as the contributions from successive output samples are included (in fact, we treat them in groups of 10).
7. Finally, the output sample sequence $y[n]$ is used to provide estimates of the output mean and variance. These are compared with the theoretical predictions.

You may find it valuable to run the program with different forms of processor impulse response $h[n]$, bearing in mind that the program is demonstrating theoretical results represented by equations (5.2), (5.9), (5.12) and (5.13). Note that although the shapes of the various parts of the screen plot are significant, their vertical scales are not. This is because we have normalised at various points in the program to ensure a suitable vertical range.

The computer demonstration concentrates on processing in the time domain. We have not illustrated the frequency domain relationship given by equation (5.14), because most people find it a great deal easier to visualise.

You may have noticed that we have not so far discussed the effects of linear processing on a sequence's amplitude distribution. Such effects are rather harder to quantify and predict than the ones we have so far investigated, but we will have something to say about them towards the end of the following section.

5.2 White noise through a filter

In the previous section we saw how various widely-used statistical measures of a random sequence are modified by linear processing. A particular case of this occurs when white noise is passed through a digital filter. The situation arises so often in DSP theory and practice that it merits special attention.

We introduced the concept of white noise towards the end of section 4.2.4. Basically, any random digital sequence in which adjacent sample values are completely uncorrelated may be described as 'white'. Its ACF consists of an isolated impulse at $m = 0$ (corresponding to zero time shift); and in the frequency domain, its power spectrum is 'flat' – in other words, its energy is evenly distributed throughout the frequency range.

As we mentioned earlier, it is the form of the ACF and power spectrum which determines whether or not noise is white. 'Whiteness' does not imply any particular form of amplitude distribution. To reinforce this point we show, in figure 5.4, portions of three white-noise sequences having gaussian, uniform and binary (two-level) amplitude distributions respectively. All these sequences have zero mean value, and would autocorrelate

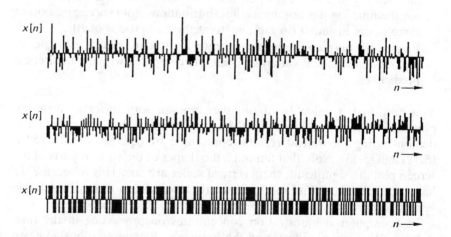

Figure 5.4 Portions of three white-noise sequences (*abscissae: 320 samples*)

to a single impulse at $m = 0$; all have an even distribution of spectral energy.

Although we are concentrating in this section on white *noise*, it is important to realise that many digital *signals* – for example, those representing speech in a digital communications system – are also more or less white. Indeed, from the communications theory point of view a 'white' sequence contains the maximum possible amount of information, since it is completely unpredictable in advance. When such a signal arrives at the receiving end and is decoded, the maximum amount of information is retrieved. This leads to the apparent paradox that a white sequence, if it represents unwanted noise, is the most chaotic possible; whereas if it represents a signal, it carries the greatest possible amount of information. But whether such a sequence represents unwanted noise or a wanted signal, it is clearly essential to be able to predict the effects of linear processing upon it. If it is noise, then we may wish to specify a filter which will reduce it as much as possible; if it is a signal, we may need to enhance it. As before, such measures as the mean, variance, ACF and power spectrum are likely to be of most interest.

The various input–output relationships derived in the previous section still hold good; but fortunately they are considerably simplified in the case of a white input sequence. Theoretical treatments of this topic often assume an input having zero mean value and unit variance, and we will do the same here. Such a sequence has an ACF consisting of a single, isolated, unit impulse at $m = 0$ (representing its mean-square value, which is the same as the variance since the mean is zero). Thus the statistical properties of the input noise are

$$m_x = 0; \quad \sigma_x^2 = 1; \quad \phi_{xx}[m] = \delta[m] \tag{5.15}$$

Furthermore, equation (4.17) gives

$$P_{xx}(\Omega) = \sum_{m=-\infty}^{\infty} \phi_{xx}[m] \exp(-j\Omega m) = \exp(-j\Omega m) \Big|_{m=0} = 1 \tag{5.16}$$

confirming that the sequence's power spectrum is 'flat', or white.

If we pass such a sequence through an LTI filter, the mean value of the output, m_y, must also be zero. As far as the output ACF is concerned, equation (5.9) reduces to

$$\phi_{yy}[m] = \sum_{q=-\infty}^{\infty} \phi_{xx}[m-q]j[q] = \sum_{q=-\infty}^{\infty} \delta[m-q]j[q] = j[m] \tag{5.17}$$

Thus $\phi_{yy}[m]$ is the same as the autocorrelation sequence of the filter itself. The output variance, obtained from equation (5.12), is

$$\sigma_y^2 = \phi_{yy}[0] - m_y^2 = \phi_{yy}[0] = j[0] \tag{5.18}$$

In the frequency domain, equation (5.14) shows that the output power spectrum has the same form as the squared-magnitude response of the filter.

Hence we may summarise the statistics of the noise at the output of the filter as

$$m_y = 0; \quad \sigma_y^2 = j[0]; \quad \phi_{yy}[m] = j[m]; \quad P_{yy}(\Omega) = |H(\Omega)|^2 \tag{5.19}$$

It may be helpful to illustrate these results with a computer. We will also use the opportunity to discuss the effects of linear processing on a sequence's amplitude distribution.

For the computer demonstration, let us consider the effects of passing a white-noise sequence with zero mean and unit variance into four different digital filters, with impulse responses shown on the left-hand side of figure 5.5. There is no particular significance in the choice of these filters – except that their impulse responses are simple in form and, as we shall see, neatly illustrate a number of important ideas. The first two filters, labelled (a) and (b), produce a simple moving average (low-pass) effect; the third one, labelled (c), is high-pass; and the fourth is a simple bandpass filter which accentuates input frequencies having around 16 samples per cycle.

The corresponding autocorrelation sequences are shown on the right-hand side of the figure. Each may easily be deduced by sliding the relevant impulse response over itself, cross-multiplying and summing all products. Note however that unlike the case of an infinite-energy random sequence, we do not take a long-term average of the result (which would be zero). The autocorrelation functions we obtain here are relevant to finite-duration sequences.

In each case the central value of the autocorrelation sequence, $j[0]$, is unity. This is because we have deliberately chosen the sample heights in $h[n]$ such that their sum of squares is unity. Referring back to equation (5.18) we see that this will produce unit output variance. Thus the average size of output fluctuations will be similar for all four filters – even though their filtering action is quite different.

From equation (5.17) we see that the output ACF in each case is expected to be the same as $j[m]$. Hence the autocorrelation sequences in figure 5.5 also define the time-domain statistics of the filtered noise.

Figure 5.6 shows the typical effects of feeding white noise into each of the filters in turn. A portion of white noise – in this case binary noise with values ± 1 – is shown at the top of the figure. It has zero mean and unit

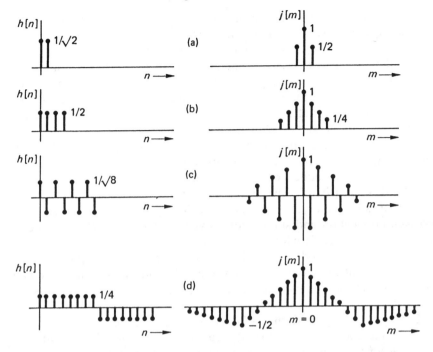

Figure 5.5   Impulse responses and autocorrelation sequences of four digital filters

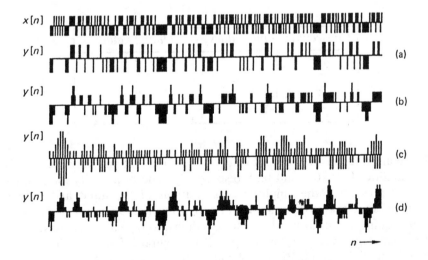

Figure 5.6   White noise processed by the four filters of figure 5.5 (*abscissae: 320 samples*)

variance. Below are shown typical output sequences from the filters. Note the simple low-pass, or smoothing, action of filters (a) and (b); the high-pass action of (c); and the bandpass action of (d). All plots have been drawn to the same vertical scale, and their variances are clearly similar – as predicted. It is also interesting to refer back to figure 5.5, noting the visual relationship between the predicted ACF and the actual sequence in each case (bear in mind that the horizontal scales are very different in the two figures, the sample values in figure 5.6 being contiguous).

The use of a binary input in figure 5.6 also gives us a good opportunity to discuss the general effects of linear processing on the amplitude distribution of a random sequence. You may recall that figure 5.1 illustrated a graphical approach to convolution, in which the impulse response of a processor is laid out backwards beneath the input sequence, followed by cross-multiplication and summation to yield a particular output value. If the input sequence is white noise, it is clear that each output value is formed as a weighted sum of completely uncorrelated input samples. Furthermore, if the input is binary white noise, and we consider a simple processor such as a moving-average filter, it is fairly easy to quantify the situation.

Let us start by considering a 2-term moving-average filter of the type already illustrated in part (a) of figures 5.5 and 5.6. To simplify the discussion we will assume impulse response terms equal to 1.0 rather than $1/\sqrt{2}$. In this case each output sample is formed as the sum of two consecutive inputs. Assuming the binary input noise has values of ± 1, the following four situations are equiprobable:

Consecutive input values	Output value
1, 1	2
1, −1	0
−1, 1	0
−1, −1	−2

There are three distinct output values of 2, 0 and −2; and they occur with probabilities 0.25, 0.5 and 0.25 respectively. The probability mass functions representing the amplitude distributions of the input and output sequences are therefore as shown in part (a) of figure 5.7.

It is quite straightforward, if a little tedious, to repeat the exercise for a 4-term moving-average filter (see part (b) of figures 5.5 and 5.6). There are now 16 possible combinations of 4 consecutive inputs, and 5 distinct output values from the filter. The corresponding probability mass function, again assuming impulse response weights equal to 1.0, is shown in part (b) of figure 5.7. Note the increasing spread of the distribution, and the low probabilities associated with its extreme values (± 4).

We cannot offer a formal proof here, but in fact the output probability functions shown in the figure may be found quite easily by successive self-convolution of the input function. Thus if we convolve p_{x_n} with itself, we get the output function for the 2-term filter; if we convolve it with itself 3 times, we get the output function for the 4-term filter – and so on. Successive convolutions, representing filters with more and more impulse response terms, produce output amplitude distributions with more and more spread, and probabilities which diminish rapidly towards the 'tails'.

A simple convolution of this kind works because we have taken all impulse response weights as unity. If the weightings are different from one another, there are more distinct output values and the situation is harder to analyse. However, in general, as we increase the number of impulse response terms (producing a more complex filter of reduced bandwidth), it is clear that each output sample will be formed from a larger number of inputs. And as noted in section 4.2.1, when we add together many independent random variables to produce a new random variable, the latter tends to have a gaussian distribution. We may therefore expect that any form of LTI processing of white noise will produce an output which tends towards the gaussian – regardless of the amplitude distribution on the input side. Such a tendency is already visible in figure 5.7. And if you refer to parts (c) and (d) of figure 5.6, you will see examples of output sequences, formed from 8 and 16 successive inputs respectively, which are considerably closer to the gaussian.

These ideas are important because they show why a wide variety of linear algorithms, acting on random sequences, tend to produce gaussian

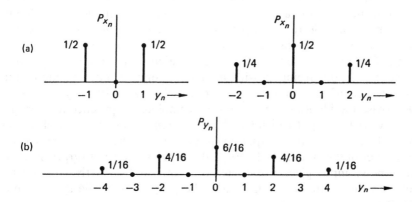

Figure 5.7 Probability mass functions: (a) at the input and output of a 2-term moving average filter; (b) at the output of a 4-term filter

forms of amplitude distribution. Furthermore, a gaussian form of input distribution is always preserved by linear processing (even though its mean and variance may be modified). This helps explain why gaussian random variables have achieved such prominence in DSP theory and practice.

5.3   System identification by cross-correlation

In section 4.2.6 we saw how a cross-correlation function (CCF) can be used to indicate the frequencies, or frequency ranges, held in common between two random sequences $x[n]$ and $y[n]$. And in the example illustrated in figure 4.10, we hinted strongly that if $x[n]$ represents the input to an LTI processor, and $y[n]$ represents the output, then the form of their CCF must contain information about the properties of the processor itself. It is this topic – often referred to as *system identification by cross-correlation* – which we wish to explore more carefully in this section.

At first sight it may seem strange that a statistical comparison of random input and output sequences can yield useful information about a deterministic system or processor. The important point is, of course, that we must work with lengthy portions of input and output; any practical estimate of the CCF will be subject to statistical variability – and only if we reduce this to manageable levels can we hope to obtain a reliable identification.

Why might we wish to explore an unknown system in this way? There are several interrelated reasons. Firstly, a system often has a certain amount of random noise present at its input (and therefore also at its output) during normal operation, and we may be able to use this to assess the CCF. On other occasions it may be beneficial to disturb the system with a random input signal, rather than (say) an impulse or step function. Indeed, it is often possible to inject a low-level random test signal without affecting normal operation. Such possibilities have made the technique attractive in a wide range of practical situations, in such diverse fields as electronic circuits, aerospace, biomedicine and seismology.

It is fairly easy to see that if we are to identify an unknown system or processor by disturbing it with a random input, then that input must contain a significant amount of all frequencies transmitted by the system. Otherwise the identification cannot be complete. In practice it is usual to employ a white input which has, by definition, a flat spectrum. Then any 'non-whiteness' in the output must be due to the frequency-selective properties of the system itself. Viewed in this way, it is not surprising that a white-noise input gives a particularly simple and attractive relationship between the input–output CCF and the properties of the system under investigation.

We can develop this idea quantitatively by recalling that the CCF of two sequences equals their average, or expected, cross-product, as a function of the time shift between them. Thus we may write:

$$\phi_{xy}[m] = E\{x[n]\,y[n + m]\} \tag{5.20}$$

Now the output sequence $y[n]$ may be expressed as the convolution of $x[n]$ with the impulse response $h[n]$ of the system or processor (see equation (5.1)). Therefore

$$\phi_{xy}[m] = E\left\{x[n] \sum_{k=-\infty}^{\infty} x[n + m - k]\,h[k]\right\}$$

$$= \sum_{k=-\infty}^{\infty} \phi_{xx}[m - k]\,h[k] \tag{5.21}$$

This important result shows that the input–output CCF equals the convolution of the input ACF with the impulse response of the system.

Let us now simplify the situation by assuming a zero-mean, white-noise input of unit variance. In this case the input ACF consists of a unit impulse at $m = 0$, hence

$$\phi_{xx}[m] = \delta[m] \tag{5.22}$$

and

$$\phi_{xy}[m] = \sum_{k=-\infty}^{\infty} \delta[m - k]\,h[k] = h[m] \tag{5.23}$$

The input–output CCF is now identical to the system's impulse response; and of course, the impulse response of an LTI system or processor completely identifies it in the time domain.

Figure 5.8 illustrates the technique applied to a digital bandpass filter. At the top are shown short portions of the white-noise input sequence to the filter, and the filtered output. Below, on the left, is shown the actual impulse response of the filter (which, in this case, we know in advance!); and on the right, a computed estimate of the CCF based upon 1000 sample values of $x[n]$ and $y[n]$. In spite of a certain amount of statistical variability, there is very good tie-up between the impulse response and the CCF estimate. We could, of course, achieve an even better identification by processing longer portions of the two sequences.

So far we have concentrated on the time domain. In the frequency domain, the situation is perhaps rather easier to visualise. The convolution of input ACF and impulse response specified by equation (5.21) must be

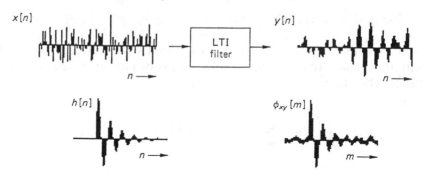

Figure 5.8   Identifying an LTI filter by cross-correlation

equivalent to multiplication of the corresponding spectral functions. These are the power spectrum and the frequency response of the system respectively. Therefore we may write:

$$P_{xy}(\Omega) = P_{xx}(\Omega)\, H(\Omega) \tag{5.24}$$

In the case of a white-noise input with zero mean and unit variance, the input power spectrum is unity (see equation 5.16)). We then have

$$P_{xy}(\Omega) = H(\Omega) \tag{5.25}$$

showing that the cross-spectrum takes the same form as the frequency response of the system.

As noted previously, the technique of system identification by cross-correlation has found widespread application. Time-domain correlation is particularly appropriate in DSP, because of the ease with which the basic operations required – time shifting, multiplication and summation – can be performed using digital hardware. Because of its practical importance, there is one other aspect of such cross-correlation which we should mention here: its resistance to certain types of *system non-linearity*.

At the end of section 4.2.6 we pointed out that cross-correlation picks out shared frequency components in two sequences, and therefore reveals only linear relationships between them. When we are using input–output cross-correlation to identify a system, any system non-linearity will tend to produce frequency components in $y[n]$ which are not present in $x[n]$. Therefore we must expect the CCF to focus on the linear part of system performance, at the expense of any non-linear part. This may or may not be an advantage. If the non-linearity is spurious or unwanted, we may be pleased to have it suppressed; but if it is an essential aspect of system performance, we obviously need to know about it. The tendency of correlation functions to ignore non-linearities is therefore valuable in some circumstances, but a nuisance in others.

Figure 5.9 illustrates the above discussion. The linear processor in this case is a second-order high-pass filter with the impulse response shown in the lower-left part of the figure. Once again, we use a gaussian white-noise input to the filter; but this time the output is subjected to a severe non-linearity by being *infinitely-clipped*. In other words each output sample is changed to ±1, depending on whether it is positive or negative. This is equivalent to ignoring all information in the output sequence apart from its zero-crossings. The short portion of the output sequence shown in the figure does indeed suggest that not very much has been retained! Nevertheless the computed CCF shown in the lower-right of the figure, again based on 1000 input and output samples, is strikingly like the actual impulse response of the linear part of the system.

We must be careful not to generalise too much from a particular example, because the degree of resistance to non-linearity depends very much on the particular case. Nevertheless, figure 5.9 helps illustrate a major feature of correlation analysis.

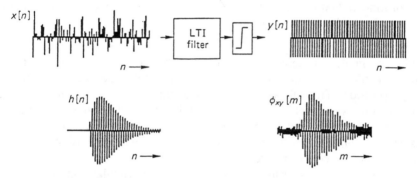

Figure 5.9 Cross-correlation in the presence of non-linearity

5.4 Signals in noise

5.4.1 Introduction

One of the most important topics in the whole of signal processing concerns the extraction of wanted signals from unwanted noise. This problem arises to some extent in almost all communication, recording and measurement situations. In communication engineering, the ability of a receiver to detect a weak signal in the presence of noise (either picked up along the transmission path, or in the receiver itself) imposes a fundamental limit on the information capacity of the channel. When recording data or analog signals, or making measurements, the reduction of spurious noise to acceptable levels is often a major preoccupation. As far as DSP is concerned, many of the techniques employed to enhance signal-to-noise ratio have their origins in analog signal processing; but others have been developed from first principles, and offer distinctive advantages of their own. In the following sections we will give a short and strictly introductory account of signals in noise, illustrating a number of key ideas and applications with the aid of a computer.

Terms such as 'recovery' and 'detection', when applied to signals in noise, are not entirely standard. It is therefore important to be clear how they will be used here:

> By *recovery*, we shall mean the extraction of a signal from noise, when the signal waveshape is not known in advance and must be preserved as accurately as possible. In such situations, we normally require *a priori* information about the frequency bands occupied by signal and noise.
>
> The term *detection* will be used when a known signal waveshape of finite duration is contaminated by noise, and we wish to find out when (or indeed if) it occurs. This type of problem arises widely in such fields as radar and sonar engineering.

When a signal, contaminated by noise, is to be recovered or detected using an LTI filter or processor, we may fortunately use the Principle of Superposition. This allows us to compute the effects on signal and noise components separately, and is a great advantage. It assumes, of course, that the noise is *added* to the signal; other types of noise contamination (such as *multiplicative*) do sometimes arise, but are much harder to analyse and will not be covered here.

It is important to bear in mind that whether a particular digital sequence is regarded as 'signal' or 'noise' depends largely on one's point of view: if wanted, it is a signal; if unwanted, it is noise. It follows that most of the previous work in this chapter is relevant to the description of signals as well as noise.

The topic of signal recovery, as defined above, is extremely wide. Here, we will concentrate on two particular types of situation which often arise in practice and are relatively easy to analyse: a comparatively narrowband signal contaminated by wideband noise; and a wideband signal contaminated by narrowband noise (such as mains-frequency interference). As far as signal detection is concerned, we will focus on a widely employed linear technique – and one which is particularly suited to digital methods – known as matched filtering. Finally we will consider the enhancement of a repetitive signal by averaging over many repetitions – a valuable technique in fields as diverse as pulse radar and biomedicine.

5.4.2 Signal recovery

*One of the most common requirements in signal recovery is to separate a comparatively narrowband signal from wideband noise. For example, in many multi-channel communications systems each individual signal is allocated its own narrow frequency slot; but random noise picked up during transmission tends to occupy the complete system bandwidth. One of the main tasks of the receiver, therefore, is to recover narrowband signals from wideband noise.

In such situations we are interested in assessing the improvement in signal-to-noise ratio which can be obtained by linear filtering. As far as the signal is concerned, it is convenient to specify an ideal bandpass filter covering the signal's bandwidth, as indicated in figure 5.10. If we also assume a linear phase response, the signal will be passed through the filter in undistorted form. Of course, we can only approximate such a filter in practice – but the ideal case indicates an upper limit to performance. As far as the noise is concerned, we need to know its spectral distribution (it may or may not be white), and then to assess the reduction in noise level through the filter. This is quite readily done using results derived previously.

*Assuming that the unwanted noise has zero mean value, then its autocorrelation and autocovariance sequences are identical, and the output noise power, or variance, from the filter is given by equation (4.19):

$$\phi_{yy}[0] = \frac{1}{2\pi} \int_{2\pi} P_{yy}(\Omega) \, d\Omega \qquad (5.26)$$

Substitution from equation (5.14) yields

$$\phi_{yy}[0] = \frac{1}{2\pi} \int_{2\pi} |H(\Omega)|^2 \, P_{xx}(\Omega) \, d\Omega \qquad (5.27)$$

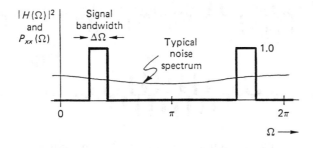

Figure 5.10

If the filter's squared-magnitude response takes the form shown in the figure, the output noise power becomes

$$\phi_{yy}[0] = \frac{1}{2\pi} \int_{2\Delta\Omega} P_{xx}(\Omega)\ d\Omega \tag{5.28}$$

In other words it is found by integrating the input noise power spectrum over the passband of the filter. A further simplification is possible if the input noise to the filter is assumed to be white, with unit variance. Its input power spectrum is then unity (see equation (5.16)), and we obtain

$$\phi_{yy}[0] = \frac{1}{2\pi} \int_{2\Delta\Omega} 1\ d\Omega = \frac{\Delta\Omega}{\pi} \tag{5.29}$$

We see that the reduction in total noise power (or variance) through the filter is simply given by the ratio of the filter bandwidth to the frequency interval π. Since the signal is assumed to be transmitted unaltered, this ratio also gives the improvement in signal-to-noise power ratio (the improvement in the amplitude ratio may, of course, be found by taking the square root).

Although this theoretical treatment is straightforward enough, its practical implementation may prove rather more awkward. Figure 5.11 simulates some of the problems, as well as the benefits, of signal recovery using an LTI filter. It is basically a time-domain equivalent of figure 5.10. The signal we have chosen is the switched sinusoid, or tone-burst, shown in

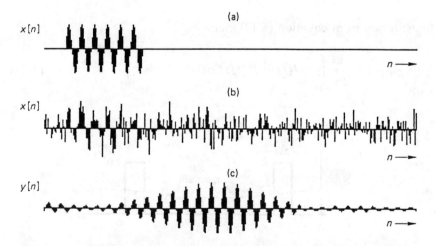

Figure 5.11   Recovering a narrowband signal from white noise (*abscissae: 320 samples*)

part (a) of the figure. It is basically narrowband, but the switch-on and switch-off cause spectral spreading around the nominal frequency of the sinusoid. In part (b) of the figure we see the signal added to white gaussian noise. It is this sequence we wish to filter in order to improve the signal-to-noise ratio.

The filter used here is a tenth-order Chebyshev bandpass design (see section 2.2.2) with its centre-frequency at the frequency of the tone-burst, a 1 dB passband ripple, and a bandwidth equal to $\pi/36$. In line with equation (5.29) we expect the average noise power to be reduced 36 times, and the standard deviation 6 times. This is borne out by the form of the filter output, shown in part (c) of the figure. Clearly, the noise reduction performance of the filter is very considerable.

However, the recovery of the signal is less impressive. Although it now stands out clearly above the residual noise, it has a slow onset and decay. These effects are not predicted by the usual steady-state analysis (including that given above), but they are a very real, and inevitable, consequence of using any linear processor. Basically the problem is that we have specified a narrowband filter in order to achieve a substantial reduction in the noise; but such a filter has a long-lived transient response, and it cannot settle quickly following a sudden change of input. We could, of course, specify a filter of wider bandwidth – but it would give an inferior performance as far as the noise is concerned. There is, in other words, a compromise to be reached between steady-state noise reduction and transient response to signal fluctuations. Although we have deliberately chosen a rather severe example to illustrate the problem, it arises to some extent in most signal-recovery situations.

It is worth making two further points. Firstly, the noise at the filter output is now narrowband (but still gaussian), and occupies the same frequency range as the signal. This is, of course, the effect of any linear filter. Secondly, the signal is considerably delayed by passage through the filter. This is an unavoidable effect, but fortunately not one which gives cause for concern in most practical applications.

We now turn to a rather different problem – that of recovering a wideband signal from narrowband noise. Here the linear processor must be some form of bandstop, or notch, filter. We demonstrated the action of such a filter on an electromyogram (EMG) signal back in section 1.1 (see figure 1.3); and computed its frequency response towards the end of section 1.4.2. Such a filter should have a gain close to unity with negligible phase shift, except over a narrow band of frequencies lying within the rejection notch. The situation is more or less the opposite of that shown in figure 5.10.

Let us illustrate with a further example drawn from biomedicine – the rejection of mains-frequency interference from an electrocardiogram (ECG), representing electrical activity of the heart. Part (a) of figure 5.12

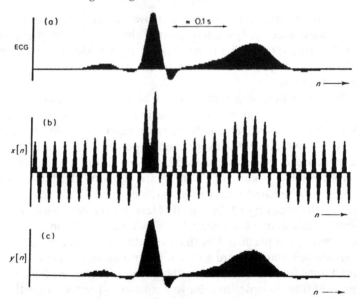

Figure 5.12 Recovering a wideband signal from narrowband noise (*abscissae: 320 samples*)

shows a typical ECG waveform, corresponding to a single heartbeat, which has been sampled at 1 kHz. In part (b) of the figure it is shown badly contaminated by sinusoidal interference at mains supply frequency – a common problem when recording biomedical signals, because of pick-up in electrode leads. It must obviously be reduced if the ECG is to have diagnostic value.

We require a notch filter similar to that used for the EMG in section 1.1, but designed for a sampling rate of 1 kHz rather than 2 kHz. An appropriate z-plane pole–zero configuration for the filter is shown in figure 5.13. A complex zero-pair is placed on the unit circle at points corresponding to the required notch frequency; and there is an adjacent complex pole-pair, with a radius just less than unity. Recalling the technique of geometrical evaluation of the Fourier Transform in the z-plane described in section 1.5.2, we see that, over most of the frequency range, pole and zero vectors drawn from the unit circle will be almost identical, giving a gain close to unity and negligible phase shift. But in the immediate vicinity of the notch frequency, the zero vectors become much smaller than the pole vectors, giving a cut-off effect. The width of the notch depends on the pole radius – the closer it is to unity, the narrower the notch. At first sight it seems we should make the notch very narrow; but that would give the filter a long-lived transient response, and run the risk that small variations

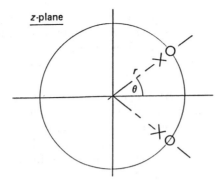

Figure 5.13   *z*-Plane poles and zeros of a bandstop filter

in mains supply frequency would fall outside the notch. A suitable compromise in this case is to place the poles at a radius of 0.975. Also, for a sampling frequency of 1 kHz and a mains frequency of 50 Hz (or alternatively, a sampling frequency of 1.2 kHz and a mains frequency of 60 Hz) the angle θ is given by

$$\frac{\theta}{\pi} = \frac{50}{500} = \frac{60}{600}, \quad \text{hence } \theta = 0.314159 \tag{5.30}$$

The filter's transfer function takes the form:

$$H(z) = \frac{Y(z)}{X(z)} = \frac{\{z - \exp(j\theta)\}\{z - \exp(-j\theta)\}}{\{z - r\exp(j\theta)\}\{z - r\exp(-j\theta)\}}$$

$$= \frac{z^2 - 2\cos\theta\, z + 1}{z^2 - 2r\cos\theta\, z + r^2} \tag{5.31}$$

Substituting the chosen values for r and θ, we obtain:

$$H(z) = \frac{z^2 - 1.9021z + 1}{z^2 - 1.8546z + 0.9506} \tag{5.32}$$

The corresponding difference equation is

$$y[n] = 1.8546y[n-1] - 0.9506y[n-2] + x[n] - 1.9021x[n-1]$$
$$+ x[n-2] \tag{5.33}$$

Returning to figure 5.12, we see the effect of the filter in part (c). The ECG signal has been very effectively recovered from the unwanted interference.

It must be admitted that the problems we have discussed in this section are fairly straightforward, since the spectral distributions of signal and noise are so different. This makes the task of separating them by linear filtering relatively easy. Although such situations quite often arise in practical DSP, on other occasions we are faced with severely overlapping spectra. The way forward is then via the theory of optimal filtering and estimation – a topic beyond the scope of this chapter, but covered in various more advanced texts (for example, references 1 and 5 in the Bibliography at the end of this book).

5.4.3 *Matched filter detection*

In the previous section we considered the problem of recovering a signal of unknown shape, using *a priori* information about the frequency bands occupied by signal and noise. A rather different situation arises when we know the shape of the signal (that is, we know not only its frequency band, but also the amplitudes and relative phases of its various components within that band), and we need to establish *when*, or indeed *if*, it occurs. A classic instance is pulse radar, let us say for Air Traffic Control. A train of pulses is sent out by the radar transmitter, and the receiver has to detect pulse echoes of similar shape, reflected from distant aircraft. The wave-shape is known in advance, and is not itself the important feature; what matters is the reliable detection of the echoes, which are often weak and badly contaminated by random noise. In this type of situation the optimum linear filter is a so-called *matched filter*.

The matched filter is very important in DSP for a further reason; it highlights the close relationships between convolution, correlation and linear filtering. You have probably noticed previously that convolution, as first described in section 1.3.2, and correlation, as discussed in sections 4.2.4 and 4.2.6, are very similar operations. In the case of convolution, we find the output of an LTI processor by laying a reversed version of the processor's impulse response beneath the input signal, then cross-multiplying and summing all terms (as illustrated in figure 1.14). With correlation, we also lay one time function beneath the other, cross-multiply and sum; the only difference is that one of the functions is not time-reversed.

The similarity is neatly illustrated by the operation of a matched filter. Consider the time-limited input signal $x[n]$ shown in figure 5.14, processed by an LTI filter whose impulse response $h[n]$ is a *reversed* version of $x[n]$. This filter is, by definition, the matched filter for this particular input signal. We may, as always, find the output signal by convolving $x[n]$ and

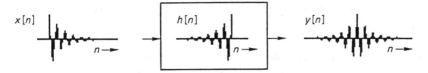

Figure 5.14   A matched filter

$h[n]$ – laying a reversed version of $h[n]$ below $x[n]$, cross-multiplying and summing all terms to produce a particular value of $y[n]$. In this case, such a convolution is exactly equivalent to forming the autocorrelation function (ACF) of $x[n]$. The resulting form of $y[n]$ is typical of an ACF – symmetrical in form, with a peak central value. We conclude that a matched filter is a form of *automatic correlator*, producing an output similar in form to the ACF of the signal to which it is matched. It summarises the tie-up between convolution, correlation, and filtering.

Of course, the output from the matched filter is a function of the time parameter n, rather than the time-shift parameter m. Furthermore, its peak central value occurs at the instant when the complete input signal has just entered the filter, rather than at $n = 0$. But the *form* of the output is identical to the ACF of the input. It is also worth noting that the type of ACF we are discussing here is relevant to a time-limited signal having finite energy: we compute the summed cross-product, but do not take a long-term average (as with an infinite-energy random sequence).

In the frequency domain, the response of a matched filter bears a simple relationship to the spectrum of the signal to which it is matched. Since the impulse response and frequency response of any LTI filter are related as a Fourier Transform pair, it follows that the frequency response in this case is

$$H(\Omega) = \sum_{n=-\infty}^{\infty} x[-n]\,\exp(-j\Omega n)$$

$$= \sum_{k=-\infty}^{\infty} x[k]\,\exp(-j(-\Omega)k) = X(-\Omega) \tag{5.34}$$

Now the spectrum $X(\Omega)$ of any real sequence can be expressed in the form

$$X(\Omega) = A(\Omega) + jB(\Omega) \tag{5.35}$$

where $A(\Omega)$ is an even function representing cosine components, and $B(\Omega)$ is an odd function representing sines. Hence

$$H(\Omega) = X(-\Omega) = A(-\Omega) + jB(-\Omega) = A(\Omega) - jB(\Omega) = X^*(\Omega)$$
$$(5.36)$$

where the asterisk denotes the complex conjugate. We see that the matched filter's frequency response is given by the complex conjugate of the signal spectrum to which it is matched. Note also that the output signal spectrum is

$$Y(\Omega) = X(\Omega) H(\Omega) = X(\Omega) X^*(\Omega) = |X(\Omega)|^2 \qquad (5.37)$$

This is what we would expect. For we have already noted in section 4.2.4 that the ACF of a signal contains the same frequencies as the signal itself, with squared magnitudes but without phase information.

We now move on to the second main task of this section – to explain why a matched filter is so often used for detecting the presence of a known, time-limited signal in the presence of noise.

Since the signal waveform is assumed to be known in advance, we do not need a filter which transmits it in undistorted form. A better criterion is that the filter should give the greatest possible instantaneous output whenever the signal waveform occurs. The detection task is then reduced to searching the filtered signal-plus-noise waveform for large peaks. This is easily accomplished by an electronic circuit or computer program.

It may be shown theoretically that, if the noise has a constant power spectrum over the frequency range occupied by the signal, then the improvement in signal-to-noise (S:N) ratio produced by a matched filter is the best possible (or, more correctly, it is the best possible with any linear filter; and in the restricted case of gaussian noise, it is the best possible with any filter, linear or non-linear).

Let us illustrate with an example, which is based on Computer Program 10 listed in appendix A. Part (a) of figure 5.15 shows two versions of a finite-length signal, separated from one another along the time axis (as in figure 5.14, there is no particular signficance in this choice of signal). When the sequence is fed into the appropriate matched filter, we get an output consisting of two versions of the ACF, as shown in part (b). Now suppose the initial sequence is badly contaminated by white gaussian noise, as in part (c) of the figure. This makes the signal occurrences very difficult to detect, because the noise occasionally rises to levels comparable with the peak signal value. The advantage of processing with the matched filter is confirmed by part (d). Two signal peaks, corresponding to the two central ACF values, now stand out well, and would be easy to locate using a threshold detector.

Of course, even a matched filter is not perfect – it inevitably allows through noise lying within its passband. Note also that matched filter detection involves a time delay equal to the duration of the signal, because

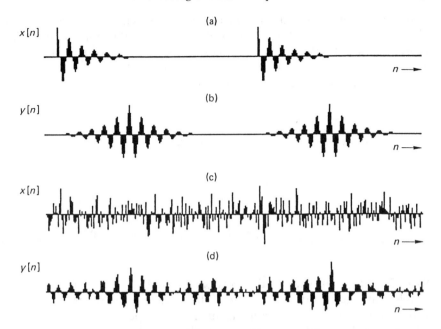

Figure 5.15 Matched filter detection of a repetitive signal in noise
(*abscissae: 320 samples*)

a peak output value always occurs at the instant when the complete input signal has just 'entered' the filter. However such a delay is not usually a practical disadvantage.

Computer Program 10 generates the input signal, adds a selected amount of gaussian noise, reverses the input signal to produce the required impulse response, and then convolves input and impulse response to produce the output. The plots in figure 5.15 represent two separate runs of the program – one without noise, the other with noise – and you may like to reproduce them for yourself. The input signal and noise can easily be changed, giving a good idea of matched filter performance for a variety of signal waveshapes and noise levels.

If we assume the noise is white, the improvement in S:N ratio is easily calculated. Let us denote the peak signal value at the filter input by $\hat{x}$. At the output the peak signal value is given by the central value of the ACF:

$$\phi_{xx}[0] = \sum_{n=-\infty}^{\infty} (x[n])^2 \tag{5.38}$$

We showed in section 5.2 that the variance of white noise increases by a factor $j[0]$ as it passes through a linear filter, where $j[0]$ is the central value of the filter's autocorrelation sequence. In the special case of a matched filter, $j[0]$ equals $\phi_{xx}[0]$ as defined above. Hence the noise amplitude, expressed as a standard deviation, increases by the square root of $\phi_{xx}[0]$. The S:N ratio improvement due to matched filtering (expressed in terms of signal and noise amplitudes) is therefore:

$$\left(\frac{\text{output peak signal}}{\text{input peak signal}}\right) \bigg/ \left(\frac{\text{output noise}}{\text{input noise}}\right) = \frac{\phi_{xx}[0]}{\hat{x}} \bigg/ \phi_{xx}[0]^{1/2}$$

$$= \frac{\left\{ \sum_{n=-\infty}^{\infty} (x[n])^2 \right\}^{1/2}}{\hat{x}}$$

(5.39)

Note that the improvement depends on the sum of squares of all signal samples (in other words, on the signal's total energy) and on its peak value prior to filtering – but not on its detailed waveshape.

Computer Program 10, as described above, uses a signal with a peak value of unity and a sum of squares equal to 5.887. The improvement in S:N ratio due to matched filtering in this case (illustrated by figure 5.15) is therefore:

$$5.887^{1/2} = 2.43 \quad \text{or} \quad 7.7 \text{ dB}$$

(5.40)

You may wonder whether the S:N ratio of the output sequence shown in part (d) of figure 5.15 could be improved by another matched filtering operation. After all, we know the new form of the 'signal', and it is still corrupted by noise. The answer is that no further improvement is possible, because the signal components have been optimally arranged in phase by the first matched filter to yield the largest possible peak, and the signal and noise now have the same spectral distribution. Another linear filter, which could only adjust spectral amplitudes and/or phases, would offer no advantage.

Following matched filtering, there is still a final decision to make about when, or if, a signal waveform occurs. This is a statistical problem which cannot be answered with certainty: even if a particular feature looks like a signal peak, it is at least possible that it is only noise; and when a signal is in fact present, the noise may happen to subtract from it and make it invisible. In the case of gaussian noise, the probabilities associated with these two types of error are well documented (see, for example, reference 16 and 19 in the Bibliography at the end of this book), and are found to be crucially dependent on noise level. We conclude that even though a matched filter is the optimum linear processor in this type of situation, it can only succeed if the noise level at its input is sufficiently low.

5.4.4 Signal averaging

When recovering or detecting a signal in the presence of noise, we need to take advantage of all its known characteristics. So far our only assumptions have been about bandwidth or waveshape. However if a deterministic signal of finite duration, obscured by noise, is known to repeat itself at particular instants of time, a further technique known as *signal averaging* may be used to clarify it, Such situations arise quite often in experiments of the *stimulus-response* type, where a series of brief stimuli is applied to a system under investigation. Such experiments are widely used in the biomedical sciences, and parallel the operation of a pulse radar system, where a train of radio-frequency pulses, transmitted at known instants, produces a corresponding series of echoes from a distant target such as an aircraft.

Suppose, for example, we wish to assess the impulse response of a system or processor, but our measurements are subject to additive noise. We repeat the input impulse many times, and produce a whole series of responses, as shown in figure 5.16 (actually, the noise level is so great in the figure that it is extremely hard to detect individual responses by eye). Provided the noise is largely or wholly uncorrelated between successive responses, we may now add together (or average) successive versions of

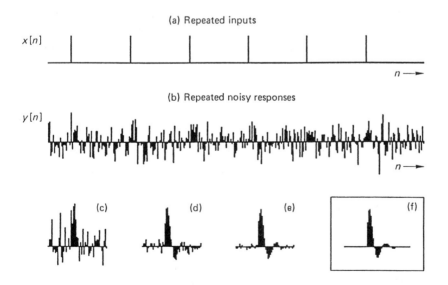

Figure 5.16   Signal averaging (*abscissae: 320 and 50 samples*)

the response in order to 'rescue' the signal from the background noise. The reason for this is that each response is composed of two parts – a deterministic signal, and unwanted random noise. When we add a number of responses together, the signal portion is truly additive; but noise fluctuations, being uncorrelated, tend to average out to zero.

In the figure, we have shown the effect of averaging over (c) 5 responses, (d) 50 responses and (e) 500 responses. Also shown inset, at the bottom right of the figure, is the 'pure' signal (which, in this example, represents the impulse response of a second-order digital filter). Clearly, the more responses we average, the better the S:N ratio becomes.

If (as in the figure) the noise is white and therefore completely uncorrelated between successive versions of the response, the improvement in S:N ratio is readily calculated. As previously mentioned in section 4.2.2, the variance of the sum of uncorrelated random sequences equals the sum of their individual variances. Therefore if we sum k versions of the noisy response, we get a signal increased in size by a factor k. The noise variance is increased by the same factor, and its standard deviation by $\sqrt{k}$. The S:N ratio, expressed in terms of amplitudes, therefore improves by $\sqrt{k}$. In part (c) of the figure this improvement is $\sqrt{5}$, or 7 dB; in part (d), $\sqrt{50}$ or 17 dB; and in part (e), $\sqrt{500}$ or 27 dB.

If the noise is partially correlated between successive input impulses, the improvement in S:N ratio will generally be less than $\sqrt{k}$ – and more difficult to predict. A somewhat different problem arises if the noise contains strictly periodic components, such as at mains supply frequency; in such cases the noise will clearly be correlated between successive presentations of the input if the latter is also strictly periodic. A convenient way around the difficulty is to apply the input stimuli at irregular instants. Finally it is worth noting that signal averaging can be supplemented by conventional filtering, to further enhance the S:N ratio – assuming, of course, that signal and noise have different spectral distributions.

Problems

5.1. A random input signal with unit mean value is applied to digital filters specified by the following difference equations:

(a) low-pass $\quad y[n] = \displaystyle\sum_{k=0}^{5} x[n - k]$

(b) high-pass $\quad y[n] = -0.8y[n - 1] + x[n]$

(c) bandpass $\quad y[n] = 1.5y[n - 1] - 0.85y[n - 2] + x[n]$.

In each case, find the mean value of the random output.

5.2. A digital processor has the transfer function:

$$H(z) = \frac{(z + 1)(z^2 + 1)}{z^2 - 2r\cos\theta z + r^2}$$

If its input signal is a random sequence with unit mean value, express the mean value of the output in terms of r and θ.

5.3. A 3-point moving-average filter is used to smooth a random sequence. Figure P5.3 shows the impulse response of the filter, and the autocorrelation function (ACF) of the input sequence.

(a) What is the variance of the input sequence?
(b) Sketch the ACF of the output sequence.
(c) Find the variance of the output sequence.
(d) Derive an expression for the output power spectrum.

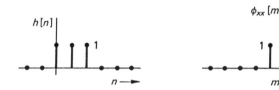

Figure P5.3

5.4. White digital noise with zero mean and unit variance is processed by a digital filter having the following difference equation:

$$y[n] = y[n - 1] + x[n] - x[n - 8]$$

Specify the ACF of the output noise, and find its variance.

5.5. Two different LTI processors are to be identified using random input signals, by the method of input–output cross-correlation. Parts (a) and (b) of figure P5.5 show the input ACF and input–output CCF in the two cases.

Find expressions for the frequency responses of the processors.

5.6. Discuss the advantages, and limitations, of system identification by input–output cross-correlation.

5.7. A narrowband digital signal is contaminated by white noise. What improvement in signal-to-noise (S:N) ratio may theoretically be achieved using a linear filter, if the signal occupies the following frequency band(s) within the range $0 \leqslant \Omega \leqslant \pi$? Express your answers in decibels (dB).

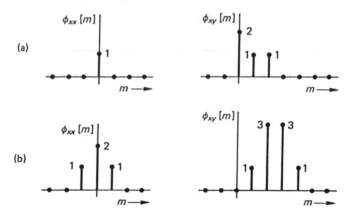

Figure P5.5

(a) 0 to $\pi/10$
(b) $\pi/50$ to $2\pi/50$
(c) $\pi/12$ to $\pi/10$, and $\pi/24$ to $\pi/20$.

Why would these figures not be fully achieved in practice?

5.8. A notch filter for removing mains-frequency interference from an ECG is described in section 5.4.2 of the main text.

By considering the z-plane pole–zero configuration of the filter, and using the technique of geometrical evaluation of the Fourier Transform in the z-plane, find the approximate width of the filter's rejection notch (in Hz), measured to the -3 dB points. Assume a sampling frequency of 1 kHz.

5.9. Explain how the concept of matched filtering illustrates the links between convolution and correlation, considered as DSP operations.

5.10. By modifying Computer Program 10 in appendix A, investigate matched filter detection for various signal waveshapes and noise levels.

5.11. Three time-limited signals have the following non-zero sample values:

(a) 4, 3, 2, 1
(b) −2, 4, −2, 1, 1, 2
(c) 1, −1, 1, −1, 1, −1.

Each is to be detected in the presence of white noise by using the appropriate matched filter. Estimate the expected improvement in S:N ratio in each case, giving your answer in dB.

Explain clearly why the improvement in part (b) is the same as in part (a).

5.12. In an experiment of the stimulus-response type, the response is obscured by additive white noise. Signal averaging is to be used to enhance the S:N ratio. How many repetitions of the stimulus will be needed to improve the S:N ratio by (a) 20 dB and (b) 50 dB?

5.13. In what circumstances, or under what conditions, are the following true?

(a) A random input sequence, applied to an LTI processor, produces a random output having zero mean value.

(b) The variances of random input and output signals of an LTI processor are identical.

(c) The output ACF from an LTI processor is identical in form (but not necessarily in scale) to the input ACF.

(d) The central, peak, values of a random signal's autocorrelation and autocovariance functions are the same.

(e) A noise input to a linear filter gives rise to an output whose ACF is identical to the autocorrelation sequence of the filter itself.

(f) A matched filter fails to give any improvement in signal-to-noise ratio.

Appendix A: Computer Programs

A.1 List of programs and introductory notes

Program 1: Digital convolution
Program 2: Discrete Fourier Series
Program 3: Non-recursive filter design
Program 4: Poles and zeros of Butterworth and Chebyshev filters
Program 5: Filter magnitude response
Program 6: Fast Fourier Transform (FFT)
Program 7: Probability mass functions
Program 8: Estimates of mean and variance
Program 9: Processing random sequences
Program 10: Matched filtering

The programs are complete and ready to run, and although they are not described in any detail, you should have little difficulty in understanding how they are organised if you have followed the relevant section(s) in the main text. The programs have been kept as simple as possible, using few of the available BASIC and PASCAL statements and procedures. Graphical outputs are all based on a single graphics instruction, which draws a straight line between two points on the screen. Embellishments such as axis labels have been avoided. The programs should therefore run on a wide range of computers with few, if any, modifications.

The BASIC programs have been developed on an IBM-compatible personal computer, working in graphics mode. Graphical outputs are generally best displayed with a resolution of 320×200 pixels – apart from Computer Program 6, which requires 640×200 pixels. To run these programs you will need to have BASICA or its equivalent.

The PASCAL programs have been developed on an IBM-compatible personal computer using Turbo-PASCAL version 4.0. To make them suitable for version 3.0 as well, we use procedures GRAPHMODE $(320 \times 200$ pixels), HIRES $(640 \times 200$ pixels) and DRAW. Version 3.0 graphics are supported in version 4.0 by the unit GRAPH3, which is included in a USES clause at the start of each program. To run these programs you will need a PASCAL compiler.

A.2 BASIC Programs

BASIC Computer Program 1: Digital convolution

```
100 REM ********* PROGRAM NO.1    DIGITAL CONVOLUTION *********
110 REM
120 DIM X(320),Y(320),H(60)
130 REM *************** DEFINE INPUT SIGNAL  ****************
140 FOR N=60 TO 320
150 X(N)=SIN(2*3.1415927£*N/60)+SIN(2*3.1415927£*N/10):NEXT N
160 REM
170 REM ****  DEFINE IMPULSE RESPONSE (MAX NO. OF TERMS=60)  ****
180 FOR N=1 TO 10:H(N)=.1:NEXT N
190 REM
200 REM ********* CONVOLVE INPUT AND IMPULSE RESPONSE *********
210 FOR N=61 TO 320:FOR K=1 TO 60
220 Y(N)=Y(N)+H(K)*X(N-K)
230 NEXT K:NEXT N
240 REM ***  NORMALISE SIGNALS TO MAX VALUE OF UNITY FOR PLOT ***
250 MX=0:MY=0:FOR N=1 TO 320:IF ABS(X(N))>MX THEN MX=ABS(X(N))
260 IF ABS(Y(N))>MY THEN MY=ABS(Y(N))
270 NEXT N
280 FOR N=1 TO 320:X(N)=X(N)/MX:Y(N)=Y(N)/MY:NEXT N
290 REM
300 REM ******** PLOT HORIZONTAL AXIS AND INPUT SIGNAL  ********
310 CLS:LINE(0,50)-(320,50)
320 FOR N=1 TO 320:LINE(N,50)-(N,50-X(N)*30):NEXT N
330 REM ******** PLOT HORIZONTAL AXIS AND OUTPUT SIGNAL  *******
340 LINE(0,150)-(320,150)
350 FOR N=1 TO 320:LINE(N,150)-(N,150-Y(N)*30):NEXT N
360 REM ***********************************************************
```

BASIC Computer Program 2: Discrete Fourier Series

```
100 REM ******** PROGRAM NO.2   DISCRETE FOURIER SERIES ********
110 REM **  64 REAL SAMPLE VALUES, SPECTRAL MAGNITUDE & PHASE  **
120 DIM X(64),AR(64),AI(64),MAG(64),PHASE(64)
130 FOR N=1 TO 64
140 B=2*3.141593*(N-1)
150 X(N)=SIN(B/64)+COS(B/16)+.6*COS(B/8)+.5*SIN(B/4)
160 NEXT N
170 FOR K=1 TO 64:FOR N=1 TO 64
180 AR(K)=AR(K)+(1/64)*X(N)*COS(2*3.141593*(K-1)*(N-1)/64)
190 AI(K)=AI(K)-(1/64)*X(N)*SIN(2*3.141593*(K-1)*(N-1)/64)
200 NEXT N:NEXT K
210 REM
220 REM ******** CONVERT TO SPECTRAL MAGNITUDE & PHASE **********
230 FOR K=1 TO 64:IF ABS(AI(K))<.001 THEN AI(K)=0
240 IF ABS(AR(K))<.00001 THEN AR(K)=.00001
250 MAG(K)=SQR(AR(K)^2+AI(K)^2):PHASE(K)=ATN(AI(K)/AR(K)):NEXT K
260 REM
270 REM ****  NORMALISE TO MAXIMUM VALUE OF UNITY FOR PLOT  *****
280 M1=.001:M2=.001:M3=.001
290 FOR N=1 TO 64:IF ABS(X(N))>M1 THEN M1=ABS(X(N))
300 IF ABS(MAG(N))>M2 THEN M2=ABS(MAG(N))
310 IF ABS(PHASE(N))>M3 THEN M3=ABS(PHASE(N))
320 NEXT N
330 FOR N=1 TO 64:X(N)=X(N)/M1:MAG(N)=MAG(N)/M2
340 PHASE(N)=PHASE(N)/M3
350 NEXT N
360 REM **** PLOT SIGNAL, SPECTRAL MAGNITUDE, AND PHASE  ******
370 CLS:FOR N=1 TO 64:LINE(5*(N-1),50)-(5*(N-1),50-X(N)*25)
380 LINE(5*(N-1),120)-(5*(N-1),120-MAG(N)*30)
390 LINE(5*(N-1),160)-(5*(N-1),160-PHASE(N)*20):NEXT N
400 REM ***********************************************************
```

BASIC Computer Program 3:   *Non-recursive filter design*

```
100 REM ***************** PROGRAM NO.3 *************************
110 REM * NONRECURSIVE FILTER DESIGN BY FOURIER TRANSFORM METHOD
120 REM ***** WITH RECTANGULAR, VON HANN, OR HAMMING WINDOW ****
130 REM *** AND DECIBEL PLOT OF FREQUENCY RESPONSE MAGNITUDE ****
140 REM ********** IMPULSE RESPONSE HAS (2M+1) TERMS **********
150 REM
160 DIM SEE(200),H(200),W(320)
170 PRINT"ENTER CENTER-FREQUENCY (IN DEGREES)":INPUT A
180 W0=A*3.141593/180
190 PRINT"ENTER FILTER BANDWIDTH (IN DEGREES)":INPUT B
200 W1=B*.5*3.141593/180
210 PRINT"ENTER VALUE OF M":INPUT M
220 PRINT"SELECT WINDOW:"
230 PRINT"0=RECTANGULAR; 1=VON HANN; 2=HAMMING":INPUT X:CLS
240 REM
250 REM **************** COMPUTE WINDOW VALUES ****************
260 IF X=0 THEN A=1:B=0:C=1:GOTO 290
270 IF X=1 THEN A=.5:B=.5:C=M+1:GOTO 290
280 A=.54:B=.46:C=M
290 FOR N=1 TO M:SEE(N)=A+B*COS(N*3.141593/C):NEXT N
300 REM
310 REM *********** COMPUTE IMPULSE RESPONSE VALUES ***********
320 H0=W1/3.141593:FOR N=1 TO M
330 H(N)=(1/(N*3.141593))*SIN(N*W1)*COS(N*W0)*SEE(N):NEXT N
340 REM
350 REM *********** DRAW RECTANGULAR GRID FOR PLOT ***********
360 FOR K=0 TO 5:LINE(0,30+20*K)-(320,30+20*K)
370 LINE(64*K,30)-(64*K,130):NEXT K:LINE(319,30)-(319,130)
380 REM
390 REM ************ COMPUTE FREQUENCY RESPONSE ***************
400 FOR N=1 TO 320:FREQ=3.141593*(N-1)/320
410 W(N)=H0:FOR K=1 TO M:W(N)=W(N)+2*H(K)*COS(K*FREQ):NEXT K
420 NEXT N
430 REM *** NORMALISE TO UNITY, CONVERT TO DECIBELS, AND PLOT ***
440 MAX=0:FOR N=1 TO 320:IF ABS(W(N))>MAX THEN MAX=ABS(W(N))
450 NEXT N
460 FOR N=1 TO 320
470 DB=20*LOG(ABS(W(N))/MAX)*.4343:IF DB<-50 THEN DB=-50
480 LINE(N,130)-(N,30-2*DB):NEXT N
490 REM
500 PRINT"PRESS <RETURN> TO PRINT IMPULSE RESPONSE"
510 INPUT Y:CLS
520 PRINT"VALUES H(0) TO H(M):"
530 PRINT"(CORRECTED FOR UNITY MAXIMUM GAIN)"
540 PRINT H0/MAX;:FOR N=1 TO M:PRINT H(N)/MAX;:NEXT N
550 REM ***************************************************
```

BASIC Computer Program 4:   Poles and zeros of Butterworth and Chebyshev filters

```
100 REM ********** PROGRAM NO.4      POLES AND ZEROS OF **********
110 REM ******* BUTTERWORTH AND CHEBYSHEV DIGITAL FILTERS *******
120 DIM PR(50),PI(50)
130 PRINT"CHOOSE FILTER FAMILY: 1=BUTTERWORTH; 2=CHEBYSHEV"
140 INPUT FF:PRINT"CHOOSE FILTER TYPE:"
150 PRINT"  1=LOWPASS; 2=HIGHPASS; 3=BANDPASS":INPUT FT
160 PRINT"FILTER ORDER":INPUT N:IF FT>2.5 THEN N=N/2:GOTO 200
170 PRINT"CUT-OFF FREQUENCY (DEGREES)":INPUT F1:ST=2
180 IF FT>1.5 THEN F1=180-F1
190 GOTO 220
200 PRINT"LOWER,UPPER CUT-OFF FREQUENCIES (DEGREES)":INPUT F2,F3
210 F1=F3-F2:ST=1
220 IF FF>1.5 THEN PRINT"PASSBAND RIPPLE (FRACTION)":INPUT D
230 REM
240 REM ********* FIND BUTTERWORTH/CHEBYSHEV PARAMETERS *********
250 IN=N MOD 2:N1=N+IN:N2=(3*N+IN)/2-1
260 W1=3.141593*F1/360
270 C1=SIN(W1)/COS(W1):B1=2*C1:C2=C1^2:B2=.25*B1^2
280 IF FF<1.5 THEN GOTO 320
290 E=1/SQR(1/((1-D)^2)-1):X=(SQR(E*E+1)+E)^(1/N)
300 Y=1/X:A=.5*(X-Y):B=.5*(X+Y)
310 REM **** FIND REAL AND IMAGINARY PARTS OF LOW-PASS POLES ****
320 FOR K=N1 TO N2
330 T=3.141593*(2*K+1-IN)/(2*N):IF FF<1.5 THEN GOTO 360
340 C3=A*C1*COS(T):C4=B*C1*SIN(T)
350 C5=(1-C3)^2+C4^2:R=2*(1-C3)/C5-1:I=2*C4/C5:GOTO 370
360 B3=1-B1*COS(T)+B2:R=(1-B2)/B3:I=B1*SIN(T)/B3
370 M=(N2-K)*2+1
380 PR(M+IN)=R:PI(M+IN)=I:PR(M+IN+1)=R:PI(M+IN+1)=-I:NEXT K
390 IF IN=0 THEN GOTO 440
400 IF FF<1.5 THEN GOTO 420
410 R=2/(1+A*C1)-1:GOTO 430
420 R=(1-B2)/(1+B1+B2)
430 PR(1)=R:PI(1)=0
440 CLS:IF FT>2.5 THEN GOTO 500
450 REM ********** PRINT OUT Z-PLANE ZERO LOCATIONS ************
460 IF FT>1.5 THEN GOTO 480
470 PRINT"REAL ZERO, OF ORDER";N;", AT Z=-1":GOTO 660
480 PRINT"REAL ZERO, OF ORDER";N;", AT Z=1"
490 FOR M=1 TO N:PR(M)=-PR(M):NEXT M:GOTO 660
500 PRINT"REAL ZEROS, OF ORDER";N;", AT Z=1 AND AT Z=-1"
510 REM
520 REM ********* LOW-PASS TO BANDPASS TRANSFORMATION ***********
530 F4=F2*3.141593/360:F5=F3*3.141593/360:A=COS(F4+F5)/COS(F5-F4)
540 FOR M=1 TO 50 STEP 2:AR=PR(M):AI=PI(M)
550 IF ABS(AI)<.0001 THEN GOTO 600
560 FR=A*.5*(1+AR):FI=A*.5*AI
570 GR=FR*FR-FI*FI-AR:GI=2*FR*FI-AI
580 SR=(ABS(GR+(GR*GR+GI*GI)^.5)/2)^.5:SI=GI/(2*SR)
590 P1R=FR+SR:P1I=FI+SI:P2R=FR-SR:P2I=FI-SI:GOTO 630
600 H1=A*(1+AR)/2:H2=H1*H1-AR
610 IF H2>0 THEN P1R=H1+H2^.5:P2R=H1-H2^.5:P1I=0:P2I=0:GOTO 630
620 P1R=H1:P2R=H1:P1I=(ABS(H2))^.5:P2I=-P1I
630 PR(M)=P1R:PR(M+1)=P2R:PI(M)=P1I:PI(M+1)=P2I:NEXT M
640 REM
650 REM *********** PRINT OUT Z-PLANE POLE LOCATIONS ***********
660 PRINT"RADII, ANGLES OF Z-PLANE POLES:":PRINT"  R","  THETA"
670 FOR J=1 TO N STEP ST:M=J:IF IN=0 THEN GOTO 690
680 IF J=2 THEN M=N+1
690 R=(PR(M)^2+PI(M)^2)^.5
700 TH=ATN(ABS(PI(M))/ABS(PR(M)))*180/3.141593
710 IF PR(M)<0 THEN TH=180-TH
720 PRINT R;,TH:NEXT J
730 REM  ****************************************************
```

BASIC Computer Program 5:   Filter magnitude response

```
100 REM ****** PROGRAM NO.5     FILTER MAGNITUDE RESPONSE ******
110 REM ********* FROM Z-PLANE POLE AND ZERO LOCATIONS **********
120 REM
130 DIM RP(20,2),RZ(20,2),CP(20,2),CZ(20,2),H(320)
140 CLS:PRINT"NO. OF SEPARATE REAL POLES":INPUT NRP
150 IF NRP=0 THEN GOTO 190
160 PRINT"ENTER VALUE, ORDER, OF EACH IN TURN"
170 PRINT"    FOLLOWED BY <RETURN>"
180 FOR N=1 TO NRP:INPUT RP(N,1),RP(N,2):NEXT N
190 PRINT"NO. OF SEPARATE REAL ZEROS":INPUT NRZ
200 IF NRZ=0 THEN GOTO 240
210 PRINT"ENTER VALUE, ORDER, OF EACH IN TURN"
220 PRINT"    FOLLOWED BY <RETURN>"
230 FOR N=1 TO NRZ:INPUT RZ(N,1),RZ(N,2):NEXT N
240 PRINT"NO. OF COMPLEX-CONJUGATE POLE PAIRS":INPUT NCP
250 IF NCP=0 THEN GOTO 290
260 PRINT"ENTER RADIUS, ANGLE (DEGREES), OF EACH"
270 PRINT"  IN TURN, FOLLOWED BY <RETURN>"
280 FOR N=1 TO NCP:INPUT CP(N,1),CP(N,2):NEXT N
290 PRINT"NO. OF COMPLEX-CONJUGATE ZERO PAIRS":INPUT NCZ
300 IF NCZ=0 THEN GOTO 340
310 PRINT"ENTER RADIUS, ANGLE (DEGREES), OF EACH"
320 PRINT"  IN TURN, FOLLOWED BY <RETURN>"
330 FOR N=1 TO NCZ:INPUT CZ(N,1),CZ(N,2):NEXT N
340 REM
350 REM ********** COMPUTE FREQUENCY RESPONSE MAGNITUDE *********
360 FOR N=1 TO 320:W=3.141593*(N-1)/320
370 C1=COS(W):C2=COS(2*W):S1=SIN(W):S2=SIN(2*W):H(N)=1
380 IF NRP=0 THEN GOTO 410
390 FOR K=1 TO NRP:A=RP(K,1):B=RP(K,2)
400 H(N)=H(N)/((1-2*A*C1+A*A)^(B/2)):NEXT K
410 IF NRZ=0 THEN GOTO 440
420 FOR K=1 TO NRZ:A=RZ(K,1):B=RZ(K,2)
430 H(N)=H(N)*((1-2*A*C1+A*A)^(B/2)):NEXT K
440 IF NCP=0 THEN GOTO 480
450 FOR K=1 TO NCP:R=CP(K,1):T=CP(K,2)*3.141593/180
460 D=C2-2*R*COS(T)*C1+R*R:E=S2-2*R*COS(T)*S1
470 H(N)=H(N)/((D*D+E*E)^.5):NEXT K
480 IF NCZ=0 THEN GOTO 520
490 FOR K=1 TO NCZ:R=CZ(K,1):T=CZ(K,2)*3.141593/180
500 D=C2-2*R*COS(T)*C1+R*R:E=S2-2*R*COS(T)*S1
510 H(N)=H(N)*((D*D+E*E)^.5):NEXT K
520 NEXT N
530 REM ********** FIND MAXIMUM VALUE AND PRINT OUT ***********
540 CLS:MAX=0:FOR N=1 TO 320:IF ABS(H(N))>MAX THEN MAX=ABS(H(N))
550 NEXT N
560 PRINT"MAXIMUM GAIN=";MAX;"(";20*LOG(MAX)*.4343;"DB)"
570 REM
580 REM ************ DRAW RECTANGULAR GRID FOR PLOT ***********
590 FOR K=0 TO 5:LINE(0,30+20*K)-(320,30+20*K)
600 LINE(64*K,30)-(64*K,130):NEXT K:LINE(319,30)-(319,130)
610 REM
620 REM ** NORMALISE RESPONSE TO UNITY, CONVERT TO DB, AND PLOT *
630 FOR N=1 TO 320:IF ABS(H(N))<.000001 THEN H(N)=.000001
640 DB=20*LOG(ABS(H(N))/MAX)*.4343:IF DB<-50 THEN DB=-50
650 LINE(N,130)-(N,30-2*DB):NEXT N
660 REM ***************************************************************
```

BASIC Computer Program 6: *Fast Fourier Transform (FFT)*

```
100 REM *** PROGRAM NO.6        FAST FOURIER TRANSFORM (FFT) ****
110 REM
120 REM ****** DEFINE TRANSFORM LENGTH AND ENTER INPUT DATA *****
130 DIM XR(512),XI(512):N=512:M=9
140 FOR K=1 TO N:XR(K)=0:XI(K)=0:NEXT K
150 FOR K=1 TO 32:XR(K)=1:NEXT K
160 REM
170 REM ***************** PLOT INPUT DATA ********************
180 CLS:Y=60:FOR K=1 TO N:LINE(K,Y)-(K,Y-XR(K)*40):NEXT K
190 REM
200 REM *** SELECT TRANSFORM/INVERSE TRANSFORM AND PLOT OFFSET **
210 T=1:D=1
220 Y=Y+60:IF T<0 THEN D=N
230 REM
240 REM ***************** SHUFFLE INPUT DATA *****************
250 LIM1=N-1:LIM2=N/2
260 J=1:FOR I=1 TO LIM1:IF I>J-.01 THEN GOTO 290
270 X1=XR(J):X2=XI(J):
280 XR(J)=XR(I):XI(J)=XI(I):XR(I)=X1:XI(I)=X2
290 L=LIM2
300 IF L>J-.01 THEN GOTO 320
310 J=J-L:L=L/2:GOTO 300
320 J=J+L:NEXT I
330 REM
340 REM *************** IN-PLACE TRANSFORMATION ***************
350 PI=3.141593:FOR I=1 TO M:LIM1=2^(I-1):LIM2=2^(M-I)
360 FOR L=1 TO LIM2:FOR R=1 TO LIM1
370 LIM3=(R-1)+(L-1)*2*LIM1+1
380 B1=XR(LIM3):B2=XI(LIM3):C1=XR(LIM3+LIM1):C2=XI(LIM3+LIM1)
390 ARG=2*PI*(R-1)*LIM2/N:COS1=COS(ARG):SIN1=SIN(ARG)
400 X1=C1*COS1+C2*SIN1*T:X2=-C1*SIN1*T+C2*COS1
410 XR(LIM3)=B1+X1:XI(LIM3)=B2+X2
420 XR(LIM3+LIM1)=B1-X1:XI(LIM3+LIM1)=B2-X2
430 NEXT R:NEXT L:NEXT I
440 FOR K=1 TO N:XR(K)=XR(K)/D:XI(K)=XI(K)/D:NEXT K
450 REM
460 REM *************** PLOT OUTPUT (MAGNITUDE) ***************
470 MAX=0:FOR K=1 TO N:MAG=(XR(K)^2+XI(K)^2)^.5
480 IF MAG>MAX THEN MAX=MAG
490 NEXT K
500 FOR K=1 TO N
510 LINE(K,Y)-(K,Y-((XR(K)^2+XI(K)^2)^.5)*40/MAX):NEXT K
520 REM
530 IF T<0 THEN GOTO 550
540 T=-1:GOTO 220
550 REM ****************************************************
```

BASIC Computer Program 7:   Probability mass functions

```
100 REM ***** PROGRAM NO.7   PROBABILITY MASS FUNCTIONS *******
110 REM
120 DIM X(300),Y(300)
130 REM
140 REM *************** UNIFORM DISTRIBUTION ****************
150 FOR K=1 TO 3000:B=INT(RND*300):X(B)=X(B)+1
160 LINE(B,50)-(B,50-X(B)):NEXT K
170 REM
180 REM ********* GAUSSIAN DISTRIBUTION (APPROXIMATE) *********
190 FOR K=1 TO 3000:C=0:FOR N=1 TO 30:C=C+RND:NEXT N
200 D=INT(C*10):Y(D)=Y(D)+1:LINE (D,180)-(D,180-Y(D))
210 NEXT K
220 REM ********************************************************
```

BASIC Computer Program 8:   Estimates of mean and variance

```
100 REM *** PROGRAM NO.8      ESTIMATES OF MEAN AND VARIANCE ***
110 REM
120 DIM X(320),M(16),V(16)
130 RANDOMIZE TIMER:CLS
140 REM
150 REM **** FORM 320 VALUES OF GAUSSIAN SEQUENCE, AND PLOT ***
160 FOR N=1 TO 320:C=0
170 FOR K=1 TO 12:C=C+RND-.5:NEXT K
180 X(N)=C:LINE(N,50)-(N,50-X(N)*10):NEXT N
190 REM
200 REM ******** ESTIMATE SAMPLE MEANS AND VARIANCES **********
210 FOR J=1 TO 16
220 FOR K=1 TO 20:N=K+20*(J-1)-1
230 M(J)=M(J)+X(N)/20:V(J)=V(J)+X(N)*X(N)/20:NEXT K
240 LINE(N,100)-(N,100-M(J)*50):LINE(N,160)-(N,160-V(J)*20)
250 NEXT J
260 PRINT "INPUT DUMMY VARIABLE":INPUT Z:CLS
270 REM
280 REM ********* ESTIMATE RUNNING MEAN AND VARIANCE *********
290 A=0:B=0:FOR N=1 TO 320
300 A=A+X(N):RM=A/N:B=B+X(N)*X(N):RV=B/N
310 LINE(N,80)-(N,80-RM*50):LINE(N,150)-(N,150-RV*20)
320 NEXT N
330 REM ********************************************************
```

BASIC Computer Program 9:   *Processing random sequences*

```
100 REM ****   PROGRAM NO.9        PROCESSING RANDOM SEQUENCES   ****
110 REM
120 DIM GN(1200),X(1200),Y(1200),H(10),J(19),XACF(101),YACF(101)
130 DIM EST(101)
140 REM ********* ENTER PROCESSOR´S IMPULSE RESPONSE ************
150 FOR N=1 TO 10:READ H(N):NEXT N
160 DATA 1,2,1,-1,-2,-1,1,2,1,0
170 REM
180 REM ****  FORM GAUSSIAN NOISE, ZERO MEAN, UNIT VARIANCE  ****
190 CLS:FOR N=1 TO 1200:C=0
200 FOR K=1 TO 12:C=C+RND-.5:NEXT K:GN(N)=C:NEXT N
210 REM
220 REM *****  LOW-PASS FILTER & ADD UNIT MEAN TO FORM X[N]  ****
230 FOR N=4 TO 1200
240 X(N)=(GN(N)+GN(N-1)+GN(N-2)+GN(N-3))*.5+1:NEXT N
250 REM
260 REM *********  PLOT 320 VALUES OF X[N] ON SCREEN  *********
270 FOR N=1 TO 320:LINE(N,50)-(N,50-X(N+100)*6):NEXT N
280 REM
290 REM ************* DEFINE AND PLOT INPUT ACF  ***************
300 FOR K=1 TO 101:XACF(K)=1:NEXT K
310 XACF(48)=1.25:XACF(49)=1.5:XACF(50)=1.75:XACF(51)=2
320 XACF(52)=XACF(50):XACF(53)=XACF(49):XACF(54)=XACF(48)
330 FOR N=1 TO 83:LINE(N,180)-(N,180-XACF(N+9)*25):NEXT N
340 REM
350 REM ******  FIND ACF OF PROCESSOR´S IMPULSE RESPONSE  *******
360 FOR K=1 TO 10:FOR L=1 TO K:J(K)=J(K)+H(L)*H(10-K+L)
370 NEXT L:NEXT K
380 FOR K=11 TO 19:J(K)=J(20-K):NEXT K
390 REM
400 REM ************ PREDICT MEAN VALUE OF OUTPUT  ************
410 SUM=0:FOR K=1 TO 10:SUM=SUM+H(K):NEXT K:MY=1*SUM
420 REM
430 REM ************ PREDICT AND PLOT OUTPUT ACF  *************
440 FOR M=10 TO 92:SUM=0:FOR K=1 TO 19
450 SUM=SUM+XACF(M-10+K)*J(K):NEXT K:YACF(M)=SUM:NEXT M
460 FOR N=1 TO 83
470 LINE(N+120,180)-(N+120,180-YACF(N+9)*50/YACF(51))
480 NEXT N
490 REM ******** CONVOLVE X[N] AND H[N] TO FORM Y[N]  *********
500 FOR N=15 TO 1200:FOR K=1 TO 10:Y[N]=Y[N]+H[K]*X[N-K]:NEXT K
510 NEXT N
520 REM ********  PLOT 320 VALUES OF Y[N] ON SCREEN  **********
530 A=9/(YACF(51))^.5
540 FOR N=1 TO 320:LINE(N,100)-(N,100-Y(N+100)*A)
550 NEXT N
560 REM ************* ESTIMATE AND PLOT OUTPUT ACF  ************
570 B=20*YACF(51):FOR K=1 TO 100:FOR M=10 TO 92:P=M-51
580 FOR L=1 TO 10:Q=10*(K-1)+L+60:EST(M)=EST(M)+Y(Q)*Y(Q+P)
590 NEXT L
600 LINE(M+227,180)-(M+227,180-EST(M)/B):NEXT M:NEXT K
610 PRINT "PRESS <RETURN> TO CONTINUE":INPUT Z:CLS
620 REM
630 REM *****  PREDICT & ESTIMATE OUTPUT MEAN AND VARIANCE  *****
640 SUM=0:FOR N=15 TO 1200:SUM=SUM+Y(N):NEXT N:MYE=SUM/1185
650 PRINT "OUTPUT MEAN (PREDICTED)=",MY
660 PRINT "OUTPUT MEAN (ESTIMATED)=",MYE
670 SUM=0
680 FOR N=15 TO 1200:SUM=SUM+(Y(N)-MY)^2:NEXT N:VARE=SUM/1185
690 PRINT "OUTPUT VARIANCE (PREDICTED)=",(YACF(51)-MY^2)
700 PRINT "OUTPUT VARIANCE (ESTIMATED)=",VARE
710 REM
720 REM  *********************************************************
```

BASIC Computer Program 10: Matched filtering

```
100 REM ********* PROGRAM NO.10    MATCHED FILTERING  *********
110 REM
120 DIM X(420),Y(420),H(100),S(100)
130 REM
140 REM **************** DEFINE INPUT SIGNAL  ****************
150 S(1)=1:S(2)=.575
160 FOR N=3 TO 60:S(N)=1.575*S(N-1)-.9025*S(N-2):NEXT N
170 REM
180 REM *****  LOAD TWO VERSIONS OF SIGNAL INTO INPUT ARRAY  ****
190 FOR N=1 TO 60:X(N+110)=S(N)
200 X(N+280)=X(N+280)+S(N):NEXT N
210 REM
220 REM *****  ADD REQUIRED AMOUNT OF WHITE GAUSSIAN NOISE  *****
230 PRINT"ENTER NOISE VARIANCE":INPUT NV
240 RANDOMIZE TIMER
250 FOR N=1 TO 420:SUM=0:FOR K=1 TO 12:SUM=SUM+RND-.5:NEXT K
260 X(N)=X(N)+NV*SUM:NEXT N
270 REM
280 REM **************** DEFINE IMPULSE RESPONSE  **************
290 FOR N=1 TO 60:H(N)=S(61-N):NEXT N
300 REM
310 REM ********* CONVOLVE INPUT AND IMPULSE RESPONSE  *********
320 FOR N=101 TO 420:FOR K=1 TO 100
330 Y(N)=Y(N)+H(K)*X(N-K):NEXT K:NEXT N
340 REM
350 REM ****  NORMALISE ARRAYS TO MAX VALUE OF UNITY FOR PLOT ***
360 MX=0:MY=0:FOR N=101 TO 420:IF ABS(X(N))>MX THEN MX=ABS(X(N))
370 IF ABS(Y(N))>MY THEN MY=ABS(Y(N))
380 NEXT N
390 FOR N=1 TO 420:X(N)=X(N)/MX:Y(N)=Y(N)/MY:NEXT N
400 REM
410 REM ********* PLOT INPUT AND OUTPUT SIGNAL ARRAYS  *********
420 CLS:FOR N=101 TO 420:LINE(N-100,50)-(N-100,50-X(N)*22):NEXT N
430 FOR N=101 TO 420:LINE(N-100,150)-(N-100,150-Y(N)*22):NEXT N
440 REM *********************************************************
```

A.3 PASCAL Programs

PASCAL Computer Program 1: Digital convolution

```
(***********   PROGRAM NO.1     DIGITAL CONVOLUTION  ***********)
program PROG01;
uses graph3;
var X: array[1..320] of real;
var Y: array[1..320] of real;
var H: array[1..60]  of real;
var N,K: integer;
var MX,MY: real;
(**********   CLEAR ARRAYS AND DEFINE INPUT SIGNAL  ***********)
begin
  for N:=1 to 320 do
    begin
      X[N]:=0; Y[N]:=0;
    end;
  for N:=60 to 320 do
    begin
      X[N]:=sin(2*3.141593*N/60)+sin(2*3.141593*N/10);
    end;
(******   DEFINE IMPULSE RESPONSE (MAX NO. OF TERMS=60)  ******)
  for N:=1 to 60 do
    begin
      H[N]:=0;
    end;
  for N:=1 TO 10 do
    begin
      H[N]:=0.1;
    end;
(***********   CONVOLVE INPUT AND IMPULSE RESPONSE  ***********)
  for N:=61 to 320 do
    begin
      for K:=1 to 60 do
        begin
          Y[N]:=Y[N]+H[K]*X[N-K];
        end;
    end;
(******   NORMALISE SIGNALS TO MAX VALUE OF UNITY FOR PLOT ******)
  MX:=0;
  MY:=0;
  for N:=1 to 320 do
    begin
      if abs(X[N])>MX then MX:=abs(X[N]);
      if abs(Y[N])>MY then MY:=abs(Y[N]);
    end;
  for N:=1 to 320 do
    begin
      X[N]:=X[N]/MX;Y[N]:=Y[N]/MY;
    end;
(**********   PLOT HORIZONTAL AXIS AND INPUT SIGNAL  **********)
  graphmode;
  draw(0,50,320,50,1);
  for N:=1 to 320 do
    begin
      draw(N,50,N,round(50-X[N]*30),1);
    end;
(**********   PLOT HORIZONTAL AXIS AND OUTPUT SIGNAL  *********)
  draw(0,150,320,150,1);
  for n:=1 to 320 do
    begin
      draw(N,150,N,round(150-Y[N]*30),1);
    end;
end.
(***************************************************************)
```

PASCAL Computer Program 2:   Discrete Fourier Series

```
(******** PROGRAM NO.2  DISCRETE-TIME FOURIER SERIES ********)
(***** 64 REAL SAMPLE VALUES, SPECTRAL MAGNITUDE & PHASE *****)
program PROG02;
uses graph3;
var X: array[1..64] of real;
var AR: array[1..64] of real;
var AI: array[1..64] of real;
var MAG: array[1..64] of real;
var PHASE: array[1..64] of real;
var N,K: integer;
var B,M1,M2,M3: real;
begin
  for N:=1 to 64 do
    begin
      AR[N]:=0;AI[N]:=0;
      B:=2*3.141593*(N-1);
      X[N]:=sin(B/64)+cos(B/16)+0.6*cos(B/8)+0.5*sin(B/4);
    end;
  for K:=1 to 64 do
    begin
      for N:=1 to 64 do
        begin
          AR[K]:=AR[K]+(1/64)*X[N]*cos(2*3.141593*(K-1)*(N-1)/64);
          AI[K]:=AI[K]-(1/64)*X[N]*sin(2*3.141593*(K-1)*(N-1)/64);
        end;
    end;
(********** CONVERT TO SPECTRAL MAGNITUDE & PHASE **********)
  for K:=1 to 64 do
    begin
      if abs(AI[K])<0.001 then AI[K]:=0;
      if abs(AR[K])<0.00001 then AR[K]:=0.00001;
      MAG[K]:=sqrt(AR[K]*AR[K]+AI[K]*AI[K]);
      PHASE[K]:=arctan(AI[K]/AR[K]);
    end;
(******* NORMALISE TO MAXIMUM VALUE OF UNITY FOR PLOT ********)
  M1:=0.001;M2:=0.001;M3:=0.001;
  for N:=1 to 64 do
    begin
      if abs(X[N])>M1 then M1:=abs(X[N]);
      if abs(MAG[N])>M2 then M2:=abs(MAG[N]);
      if abs(PHASE[N])>M3 then M3:=abs(PHASE[N]);
    end;
  for N:=1 to 64 do
    begin
      X[N]:=X[N]/M1;MAG[N]:=MAG[N]/M2;
      PHASE[N]:=PHASE[N]/M3;
    end;
(******* PLOT SIGNAL, SPECTRAL MAGNITUDE, AND PHASE ********)
  graphmode;
  for N:=1 to 64 do
    begin
      draw(5*(N-1),50,5*(N-1),round(50-X[N]*25),1);
      draw(5*(N-1),120,5*(N-1),round(120-MAG[N]*30),1);
      draw(5*(N-1),160,5*(N-1),round(160-PHASE[N]*20),1);
    end;
end.
(*****************************************************************)
```

PASCAL Computer Program 3: *Non-recursive filter design*

```pascal
(******************** PROGRAM NO.3 *****************************)
(**  NONRECURSIVE FILTER DESIGN BY FOURIER TRANSFORM METHOD  ***)
(******  WITH RECTANGULAR, VON HANN, OR HAMMING WINDOW  *******)
(******  AND DECIBEL PLOT OF FREQUENCY RESPONSE MAGNITUDE *****)
(***********  (IMPULSE RESPONSE HAS (2M+1) TERMS)  ***********)
program PROG03;
uses graph3;
var SEE: array[1..200] of real;
var H: array[1..200] of real;
var W: array[1..320] of real;
var H0,A,B,C,FREQ,MAX,DB,W0,W1: real;
var M,X,K,N,Y: integer;
label 1;
begin
  writeln('ENTER CENTER-FREQUENCY (IN DEGREES)'); readln(A);
  W0:=A*3.141593/180;
  writeln('ENTER FILTER BANDWIDTH (IN DEGREES)'); readln(B);
  W1:=B*0.5*3.141593/180;
  writeln('ENTER VALUE OF M'); readln(M);
  writeln('SELECT WINDOW:');
  writeln('0=RECTANGULAR; 1=VON HANN; 2=HAMMING'); readln(X);
(*****************  COMPUTE WINDOW VALUES  ******************)
    if X=0 then begin A:=1;B:=0;C:=1;goto 1 end;
    if X=1 then begin A:=0.5;B:=0.5;C:=M+1;goto 1 end;
    A:=0.54;B:=0.46;C:=M;
  1: for N:=1 to M do begin
       SEE[N]:=A+B*cos(N*3.141593/C);end;
(*************  COMPUTE IMPULSE RESPONSE VALUES  *************)
  H0:=W1/3.141593;
    for N:=1 to M do begin
      H[N]:=(1/(N*3.141593))*sin(N*W1)*cos(N*W0)*SEE[N];end;
(**************  DRAW RECTANGULAR GRID FOR PLOT  **************)
  graphmode;
    for K:=0 to 5 do begin
      draw(0,30+20*K,320,30+20*K,1);
      draw(64*K,30,64*K,130,1);end;
    draw(319,30,319,130,1);
(**************  COMPUTE FREQUENCY RESPONSE  *****************)
  for N:=1 to 320 do begin
    FREQ:=3.141593*(N-1)/320;W[N]:=H0;
      for K:=1 to M do begin
        W[N]:=W[N]+2*H[K]*COS(K*FREQ);
      end;
  end;
(*****  NORMALISE TO UNITY, CONVERT TO DECIBELS, AND PLOT  *****)
  MAX:=0;
    for N:=1 to 320 do begin
      if abs(W[N])>MAX then MAX:=abs(W[N]);
    end;
  for N:=1 to 320 do begin
    DB:=20*ln(abs(W[N])/MAX)*0.4343;if DB<-50 then DB:=-50;
    draw(N,130,N,round(30-2*DB),1);
  end;
  writeln('ENTER ANY INTEGER TO PRINT h[n] VALUES');
  readln (Y);
  clearscreen;
  writeln('VALUES h[0] TO h[M]):');
  writeln ('(CORRECTED FOR UNITY MAXIMUM GAIN)');
  writeln ( H0/MAX);
    for N:=1 to M do begin writeln(H[N]/MAX);end;
end.
(**************************************************************)
```

PASCAL Computer Program 4:   Poles and zeros of Butterworth and Chebyshev filters

```
(************  PROGRAM NO.4     POLES AND ZEROS OF  ************)
(*********  BUTTERWORTH AND CHEBYSHEV DIGITAL FILTERS  *********)
program PROG04;
var PR: array[1..50] of real;
var PI: array[1..50] of real;
var FF,FT,N,K,J,IR,M,M1,N1,N2,ST: integer;
var F1,D,W1,C1,C2,B1,B2,E,X,A,Y,B: real;
var T,C3,C4,C5,R,I,B3,F2,F3,F4,F5,FR,FI,GR,AR: real;
var GI,AI,SR,SI,H1,H2,P1R,P2R,P1I,P2I,TH: real;
label 1,2,3,4,5,6,7,8,9,10,11,12,13,14,15,16;
begin
        for K:=1 to 50 do begin PR[K]:=0;PI[K]:=0;end;
        writeln('CHOOSE FILTER FAMILY: 1=BUTTERWORTH; 2=CHEBYSHEV');
        readln(FF);
        writeln('CHOOSE FILTER TYPE:');
        writeln('  1=LOWPASS; 2=HIGHPASS; 3=BANDPASS'); readln(FT);
        writeln('FILTER ORDER');readln(N);if FT=3 then begin
          N:=trunc(N/2);goto 1 end;
        writeln('CUT-OFF FREQUENCY (DEGREES)');readln(F1);ST:=2;
          if FT>1 then F1:=180-F1;goto 2;
    1: writeln('LOWER,UPPER CUT-OFF FREQUENCIES (DEGREES)');
        readln(F2,F3);F1:=F3-F2;ST:=1;
    2: if FF=2 then begin writeln('PASSBAND RIPPLE (FRACTION)');
          readln(D) end;
(**********  FIND BUTTERWORTH/CHEBYSHEV PARAMETERS  **********)
        IR:=N mod 2;N1:=N+IR;N2:=trunc((3*N+IR)/2-1);
        W1:=3.141593*F1/360;C1:=sin(W1)/cos(W1);B1:=2*C1;C2:=C1*C1;
        B2:=0.25*B1*B1; if FF=1 then goto 3;
        E:=1/sqrt(1/((1-D)*(1-D))-1);
        X:=exp(1/N*ln(sqrt(E*E+1)+E));
        Y:=1/X;A:=0.5*(X-Y);B:=0.5*(X+Y);
(******  FIND REAL AND IMAGINARY PARTS OF LOW-PASS POLES  ******)
    3: for K:=N1 to N2 do begin
        T:=3.141593*(2*K+1-IR)/(2*N);if FF=1 then goto 4;
        C3:=A*C1*COS(T);C4:=B*C1*SIN(T);C5:=(1-C3)*(1-C3)+C4*C4;
        R:=2*(1-C3)/C5-1;I:=2*C4/C5; goto 5;
    4:  B3:=1-B1*cos(T)+B2;R:=(1-B2)/B3;I:=B1*sin(T)/B3;
    5:  M:=(N2-K)*2+1;
        PR[M+IR]:=R;PI[M+IR]:=I;PR[M+IR+1]:=R;PI[M+IR+1]:=-I;end;
        if IR=0 then goto 8;
        if FF=1 then goto 6;
          R:=2/(1+A*C1)-1;goto 7;
    6:    R:=(1-B2)/(1+B1+B2);
    7:    PR[1]:=R;PI[1]:=0;
    8:      if FT=3 then goto 10;
(*************  PRINT OUT Z-PLANE ZERO LOCATIONS  *************)
        if FT>1 then goto 9;
        writeln('REAL ZERO, OF ORDER ',N,', AT Z=-1');goto 13;
    9: writeln('REAL ZERO, OF ORDER ',N,', AT Z=1');
        for M:=1 to N do begin
        PR[M]:=-PR[M];end;goto 13;
   10: writeln('REAL ZEROS, OF ORDER ',N,', AT Z=1 AND AT Z=-1');
(**********  LOW-PASS TO BANDPASS TRANSFORMATION  ***********)
        F4:=F2*3.141593/360;F5:=F3*3.141593/360;
        A:=cos(F4+F5)/cos(F5-F4);
          for M1:=0 to 24 do begin M:=1+2*M1;
          AR:=PR[M];AI:=PI[M];
            if abs(AI)<0.0001 then goto 11;
            FR:=A*0.5*(1+AR);FI:=A*0.5*AI;
            GR:=FR*FR-FI*FI-AR;GI:=2*FR*FI-AI;
            SR:=sqrt(abs(GR+sqrt(GR*GR+GI*GI))/2);SI:=GI/(2*SR);
            P1R:=FR+SR;P1I:=FI+SI;P2R:=FR-SR;P2I:=FI-SI;goto 12;
```

```
11: H1:=A*(1+AR)/2;H2:=H1*H1-AR;
        if H2>0 then begin P1R:=H1+sqrt(H2);P2R:=H1-sqrt(H2);
        P1I:=0;P2I:=0;goto 12 end;
    P1R:=H1;P2R:=H1;P1I:=sqrt(abs(H2));P2I:=-P1I;
12: PR[M]:=P1R;PR[M+1]:=P2R;PI[M]:=P1I;PI[M+1]:=P2I;end;
(************* PRINT OUT Z-PLANE POLE LOCATIONS ************)
13: writeln('RADII, ANGLES OF Z-PLANE POLES:');
    writeln('         R',                       THETA');
        for J:=1 to N do begin
            if ST=1 then goto 14;
            if J mod ST=0 then goto 16;
14: M:=J;if IR=0 then goto 15;
            if J=2 then M:=N+1;
15: R:=sqrt(PR[M]*PR[M]+PI[M]*PI[M]);
    TH:=arctan(abs(PI[M])/abs(PR[M]))*180/3.141593;
        if PR[M]<0 then TH:=180-TH;writeln(R,TH);
16: end;
end.
(**********************************************************)
```

PASCAL Computer Program 5:   Filter magnitude response

```
(********* PROGRAM NO.5      FILTER MAGNITUDE RESPONSE ********)
(*********** FROM Z-PLANE POLE AND ZERO LOCATIONS ***********)
program PROG05;
uses graph3;
var RP: array[1..20,1..2] of real;
var RZ: array[1..20,1..2] of real;
var CP: array[1..20,1..2] of real;
var CZ: array[1..20,1..2] of real;
var H: array[1..320] of real;
var A,B,W,C1,C2,S1,S2,D,R,T,E,MAX,DB,BASE,EX: real;
var NRP,NRZ,N,NCP,NCZ,K: integer;
label 1,2,3,4,5,6,7,8;
begin
    writeln('NO. OF SEPARATE REAL POLES'); readln(NRP);
        if NRP=0 then goto 1;
    writeln('ENTER VALUE, ORDER, OF EACH IN TURN');
    writeln('   FOLLOWED BY <RETURN>');
        for N:=1 to NRP do begin
            readln(RP[N,1],RP[N,2]); end;
 1: writeln('NO. OF SEPARATE REAL ZEROS'); readln(NRZ);
        if NRZ=0 then goto 2;
    writeln('ENTER VALUE, ORDER, OF EACH IN TURN');
    writeln('   FOLLOWED BY <RETURN>');
        for N:=1 to NRZ do begin
            readln(RZ[N,1],RZ[N,2]); end;
 2: writeln('NO. OF COMPLEX-CONJUGATE POLE PAIRS'); readln(NCP);
        if NCP=0 then goto 3;
    writeln('ENTER RADIUS, ANGLE (DEGREES), OF EACH');
    writeln('   IN TURN, FOLLOWED BY <RETURN>');
        for N:=1 to NCP do begin
            readln(CP[N,1],CP[N,2]); end;
 3: writeln('NO. OF COMPLEX-CONJUGATE ZERO PAIRS'); readln(NCZ);
        if NCZ=0 then goto 4;
    writeln('ENTER RADIUS, ANGLE (DEGREES), OF EACH');
    writeln('   IN TURN, FOLLOWED BY <RETURN>');
        for N:=1 to NCZ do begin
            readln(CZ[N,1],CZ[N,2]);end;
```

```
(************ COMPUTE FREQUENCY RESPONSE MAGNITUDE **********)
4: for N:=1 to 320 do begin
     W:=3.141593*(N-1)/320;
     C1:=cos(W);C2:=cos(2*W);S1:=sin(W);S2:=sin(2*W);H[N]:=1;
     if NRP=0 then goto 5;
        for K:=1 to NRP do begin
           A:=RP[K,1];B:=RP[K,2];BASE:=1-2*A*C1+A*A;EX:=B/2;
           H[N]:=H[N]/(exp(EX*ln(BASE)))); end;
5:      if NRZ=0 then goto 6;
        for K:=1 to NRZ do begin
           A:=RZ[K,1];B:=RZ[K,2];BASE:=1-2*A*C1+A*A;EX:=B/2;
           H[N]:=H[N]*(exp(EX*ln(BASE)))); end;
6:      if NCP=0 then goto 7;
        for K:=1 to NCP do begin
           R:=CP[K,1];T:=CP[K,2]*3.141593/180;
           D:=C2-2*R*cos(T)*C1+R*R;E:=S2-2*R*cos(T)*S1;
           H[N]:=H[N]/(exp(0.5*ln(D*D+E*E)))); end;
7:      if NCZ=0 then goto 8;
        for K:=1 to NCZ do begin
           R:=CZ[K,1];T:=CZ[K,2]*3.141593/180;
           D:=C2-2*R*cos(T)*C1+R*R;E:=S2-2*R*cos(T)*S1;
           H[N]:=H[N]*(exp(0.5*ln(D*D+E*E)))); end;
8: end;
(************ FIND MAXIMUM VALUE AND PRINT OUT *************)
   graphmode;
   MAX:=0;
   for N:=1 to 320 do begin
     if abs(H[N])>MAX then MAX:=abs(H[N]); end;
   writeln('MAXIMUM GAIN=',20*ln(MAX)*0.4343,' dB');
(************** DRAW RECTANGULAR GRID FOR PLOT *************)
   for K:=0 to 5 do begin
   draw(0,30+20*K,320,30+20*K,1);
   draw(64*K,30,64*K,130,1);end;  draw(319,30,319,130,1);
(**** NORMALISE RESPONSE TO UNITY, CONVERT TO DB, AND PLOT ***)
   for N:=1 to 320 do begin
     if abs(H[N])<0.000001 then H[N]:=0.000001;
     DB:=20*ln(abs(H[N])/MAX)*0.4343;if DB<-50 then DB:=-50;
     draw(N,130,N,round(30-2*DB),1); end;
end.
(*********************************************************************)
```

PASCAL Computer Program 6: Fast Fourier Transform (FFT)

```
(******* PROGRAM NO.6         FAST FOURIER TRANSFORM  **********)
program PROG06;
uses graph3;
var XR: array[1..512] of real;
var XI: array[1..512] of real;
var LIM1,LIM2,LIM3,L,R,M,K,N,Y,I,J: integer;
var T,D,X1,X2,PI,B1,B2,C1,C2,ARG,SIN1,COS1,MAG,MAX: real;
label 1,2,3,4,5;
(******* DEFINE TRANSFORM LENGTH AND ENTER INPUT DATA  ********)
begin
   N:=512;M:=9;
   for K:=1 to N do begin
     XR[K]:=0;XI[K]:=0;end;
   for K:=1 to 32 do begin
     XR[K]:=1;end;
(****** PLOT INPUT DATA USING HIGH RESOLUTION GRAPHICS  *******)
   hires;
   Y:=60; for K:=1 to N do begin
     draw(K,Y,K,round(Y-XR[K]*40),1);end;
(***** SELECT TRANSFORM/INVERSE TRANSFORM AND PLOT OFFSET  ****)
   T:=1;D:=1;
 1: Y:=Y+60;IF T<0 THEN D:=N;
(********************* SHUFFLE INPUT DATA  *******************)
   LIM1:=N-1;LIM2:=trunc(N/2);J:=1;
   for I:=1 to LIM1 do begin
     if I>J-1 then goto 2;
       X1:=XR[J];X2:=XI[J];
       XR[J]:=XR[I];XI[J]:=XI[I];XR[I]:=X1;XI[I]:=X2;
 2: L:=LIM2;
 3: if L>J-1 then goto 4;
     J:=J-L;L:=trunc(L/2);goto 3;
 4: J:=J+L; end;
(***************** IN-PLACE TRANSFORMATION  ****************)
   PI:=3.141593;
   for I:=1 to M do begin
     LIM1:=trunc(exp((I-1)*ln(2)));
     LIM2:=trunc(exp((M-I)*ln(2)));
       for L:=1 to LIM2 do begin
         for R:=1 to LIM1 do begin
           LIM3:=(R-1)+(L-1)*2*LIM1+1;
           B1:=XR[LIM3];B2:=XI[LIM3];C1:=XR[LIM3+LIM1];
           C2:=XI[LIM3+LIM1];
           ARG:=2*PI*(R-1)*LIM2/N;COS1:=cos(ARG);SIN1:=sin(ARG);
           X1:=C1*COS1+C2*SIN1*T;X2:=-C1*SIN1*T+C2*COS1;
           XR[LIM3]:=B1+X1;XI[LIM3]:=B2+X2;
           XR[LIM3+LIM1]:=B1-X1;XI[LIM3+LIM1]:=B2-X2;
   end;end;end;
   for K:=1 to N do begin
     XR[K]:=XR[K]/D;XI[K]:=XI[K]/D;end;
(***************** PLOT OUTPUT (MAGNITUDE)  ****************)
   MAX:=0;
     for K:=1 to N do begin
       MAG:=sqrt(XR[K]*XR[K]+XI[K]*XI[K]);
       if MAG>MAX then MAX:=MAG;end;
     for K:=1 to N do begin
       draw(K,Y,K,round(Y-sqrt(XR[K]*XR[K]+XI[K]*XI[K])*40/MAX),1);
     end;
   if T<0 then GOTO 5;
   T:=-1;goto 1;
 5: end.
(**************************************************************)
```

PASCAL Computer Program 7: *Probability mass functions*

```
(********* PROGRAM NO.7    PROBABILITY MASS FUNCTIONS  ********)
program PROG07;
uses graph3;
var X: array[0..300] of real;
var Y: array[0..300] of real;
var K,N,B,D: integer;
var C: real;
(******************** UNIFORM DISTRIBUTION *******************)
begin
  for K:=0 to 300 do begin
    X[K]:=0;Y[K]:=0;end;
  randomize;graphmode;
    for K:=1 to 3000 do begin
      B:=trunc(random*300);X[B]:=X[B]+1;
      draw(B,50,B,round(50-X[B]),1);end;
(************ GAUSSIAN DISTRIBUTION (APPROXIMATE)  ***********)
  for K:=1 to 3000 do begin
    C:=0;for N:=1 to 30 do begin
          C:=C+random;end;
    D:=trunc(C*10);Y[D]:=Y[D]+1;
    draw(D,180,D,round(180-Y[D]),1);end;
end.
(*************************************************************)
```

PASCAL Computer Program 8: *Estimates of mean and variance*

```
(****** PROGRAM NO.8    ESTIMATES OF MEAN AND VARIANCE  ******)
program PROG08;
uses graph3;
var X: array[1..320] of real;
var M: array[1..16] of real;
var V: array[1..16] of real;
var J,K,N: integer;
var A,B,C,RM,RV,Z: real;
begin
  randomize;
  graphmode;
    for N:=1 to 16 do begin
    M[N]:=0;V[N]:=0;end;
(****** FORM 320 VALUES OF GAUSSIAN SEQUENCE, AND PLOT ******)
  for N:=1 to 320 do begin
    C:=0;for K:=1 to 12 do begin
          C:=C+random-0.5;end;
    X[N]:=C;draw(N,50,N,round(50-X[N]*10),1);
  end;
(*********** ESTIMATE SAMPLE MEANS AND VARIANCES ***********)
  for J:=1 to 16 do begin
    for K:=1 to 20 do begin
      N:=K+20*(J-1)-1;M[J]:=M[J]+X[N]/20;
      V[J]:=V[J]+X[N]*X[N]/20;end;
    draw(N,100,N,round(100-M[J]*50),1);
    draw(N,160,N,round(160-V[J]*20),1);end;
    writeln('INPUT DUMMY VARIABLE');readln(Z);clearscreen;
(*********** ESTIMATE RUNNING MEAN AND VARIANCE ***********)
  A:=0;B:=0;
    for N:=1 to 320 do begin
    A:=A+X[N];RM:=A/N;B:=B+X[N]*X[N];RV:=B/N;
    draw(N,80,N,round(80-RM*50),1);
    draw(N,150,N,round(150-RV*20),1);end;
end.
(*************************************************************)
```

PASCAL Computer Program 9: *Processing random sequences*

```
(******* PROGRAM NO.9        PROCESSING RANDOM SEQUENCES  *******)
program PROG09;
uses graph3;
var GN: array[1..1200] of real;
var X: array[1..1200] of real;
var Y: array[1..1200] of real;
var H: array[1..10] of real;
var J: array[1..19] of real;
var XACF: array[1..101] of real;
var YACF: array[1..101] of real;
var EST: array[1..101] of real;
var N,K,L,M,P,Q: integer;
var C,SUM,MY,A,B,Z,MYE,VARE: real;
begin
  randomize;
  graphmode;
    for N:=1 to 1200 do begin
      Y[N]:=0;end;
    for N:=1 to 19 do begin
      J[N]:=0;end;
    for N:=1 to 101 do begin
      EST[N]:=0;end;
(************ ENTER PROCESSOR'S IMPULSE RESPONSE  ************)
  H[1]:=1;H[2]:=2;H[3]:=1;H[4]:=-1;H[5]:=-2;
  H[6]:=-1;H[7]:=1;H[8]:=2;H[9]:=1;H[10]:=0;
(****** FORM GAUSSIAN NOISE, ZERO MEAN, UNIT VARIANCE  ******)
  clearscreen;
  for N:=1 to 1200 do begin
    C:=0;for K:=1 to 12 do begin
          C:=C+random-0.5;
        end;
    GN[N]:=C;
  end;
(******** LOW-PASS FILTER & ADD UNIT MEAN TO FORM X[N]  *******)
  for N:=4 to 1200 do begin
    X[N]:=(GN[N]+GN[N-1]+GN[N-2]+GN[N-3])*0.5+1;
  end;
(************ PLOT 320 VALUES OF X[N] ON SCREEN  ************)
  for N:=1 to 320 do begin
    draw(N,50,N,round(50-X[N+100]*6),1);
  end;
(**************** DEFINE AND PLOT INPUT ACF  ****************)
  for K:=1 to 101 do begin
    XACF[K]:=1;
  end;
  XACF[48]:=1.25;XACF[49]:=1.5;XACF[50]:=1.75;XACF[51]:=2;
  XACF[52]:=XACF[50];XACF[53]:=XACF[49];XACF[54]:=XACF[48];
  for N:=1 to 83 do begin
    draw(N,180,N,round(180-XACF[N+9]*25),1);
  end;
(********** FIND ACF OF PROCESSOR'S IMPULSE RESPONSE **********)
  for K:=1 to 10 do begin
    for L:=1 to K do begin
      J[K]:=J[K]+H[L]*H[10-K+L];
    end;
  end;
    for K:=11 to 19 do begin
      J[K]:=J[20-K];
    end;
```

```
(***************  PREDICT MEAN VALUE OF OUTPUT  ****************)
   SUM:=0;for K:=1 to 10 do begin
              SUM:=SUM+H[K];
            end;
   MY:=1*SUM;
(***************  PREDICT AND PLOT OUTPUT ACF  *****************)
   for M:=10 to 92 do begin
     SUM:=0;for K:=1 to 19 do begin
              SUM:=SUM+XACF[M-10+K]*J[K];
            end;
     YACF[M]:=SUM;
   end;
   for N:=1 to 83 do begin
     draw(N+120,180,N+120,round(180-YACF[N+9]*50/YACF[51]),1);
   end;
(************  CONVOLVE X[N] AND H[N] TO FORM Y[N]  ************)
   for N:=15 to 1200 do begin
     for K:=1 to 10 do begin
       Y[N]:=Y[N]+H[K]*X[N-K];
     end;
   end;
(*************  PLOT 320 VALUES OF Y[N] ON SCREEN  ************)
   A:=9/SQRT(YACF[51]);
     for N:=1 to 320 do begin
       draw(N,100,N,round(100-Y[N+100]*A),1);
     end;
(***************  ESTIMATE AND PLOT OUTPUT ACF  ***************)
   B:=20*YACF[51];
     for K:=1 to 100 do begin
       for M:=10 to 92 do begin
         P:=M-51;
           for L:=1 to 10 do begin
             Q:=10*(K-1)+L+60;EST[M]:=EST[M]+Y[Q]*Y[Q+P];
           end;
         draw(M+227,180,M+227,round(180-EST[M]/B),1);
       end;
     end;
   writeln('ENTER A DUMMY VARIABLE TO CONTINUE');readln(Z);
   clearscreen;
(******  PREDICT AND ESTIMATE OUTPUT MEAN AND VARIANCE  ******)
   SUM:=0;for N:=15 to 1200 do begin
              SUM:=SUM+Y[N];
            end;
   MYE:=SUM/1185;
   writeln('OUTPUT MEAN (PREDICTED)=');writeln(MY);
   writeln('OUTPUT MEAN (ESTIMATED)=');writeln(MYE);
   SUM:=0;for N:=15 to 1200 do begin
              SUM:=SUM+(Y[N]-MY)*(Y[N]-MY);
            end;
   VARE:=SUM/1185;
   writeln('OUTPUT VARIANCE (PREDICTED)=');
   writeln(YACF[51]-MY*MY);
   writeln('OUTPUT VARIANCE (ESTIMATED)=');writeln(VARE);
end.
(***********************************************************************)
```

PASCAL Computer Program 10:   *Matched filtering*

```
(************ PROGRAM NO.10      MATCHED FILTERING ************)
program PROG10;
uses graph3;
var X: array[1..420] of real;
var Y: array[1..420] of real;
var H: array[1..100] of real;
var S: array[1..100] of real;
var N,K: integer;
var NV,SUM,MX,MY: real;
begin
  for N:=1 to 420 do begin
  X[N]:=0;Y[N]:=0;end;
  randomize;
  graphmode;
(******************** DEFINE INPUT SIGNAL  ********************)
  S[1]:=1;S[2]:=0.575;
    for N:=3 to 60 do begin
      S[N]:=1.575*S[N-1]-0.9025*S[N-2];
    end;
(******* LOAD TWO VERSIONS OF SIGNAL INTO INPUT ARRAY  ******)
  for N:=1 to 60 do begin
    X[N+110]:=S[N];X[N+280]:=X[N+280]+S[N];
  end;
(******* ADD REQUIRED AMOUNT OF WHITE GAUSSIAN NOISE  *******)
  writeln('ENTER NOISE VARIANCE');readln(NV);
    for N:=1 to 420 do begin
      SUM:=0;
        for K:=1 to 12 do begin
          SUM:=SUM+random-0.5;
        end;
      X[N]:=X[N]+NV*SUM;
    end;
(***************** DEFINE IMPULSE RESPONSE  *****************)
  for N:=1 to 60 do begin
    H[N]:=S[61-N];
  end;
(*********** CONVOLVE INPUT AND IMPULSE RESPONSE  ***********)
  for N:=101 to 420 do begin
    for K:=1 to 100 do begin
      Y[N]:=Y[N]+H[K]*X[N-K];
    end;
  end;
(****** NORMALISE ARRAYS TO MAX VALUE OF UNITY FOR PLOT  ******)
  MX:=0;MY:=0;
    for N:=101 to 420 do begin
      if abs(X[N])>MX then MX:=abs(X[N]);
      if abs(Y[N])>MY then MY:=abs(Y[N]);
    end;
  for N:=1 to 420 do begin
    X[N]:=X[N]/MX;Y[N]:=Y[N]/MY;
  end;
(*********** PLOT INPUT AND OUTPUT SIGNAL ARRAYS  ***********)
  clearscreen;
    for N:=101 to 420 do begin
      draw(N-100,50,N-100,round(50-X[N]*22),1);
    end;
    for N:=101 to 420 do begin
      draw(N-100,150,N-100,round(150-Y[N]*22),1);
    end;
end.
(*************************************************************)
```

Appendix B: Tables of Fourier and z-Transforms

Table B.1   The Discrete Fourier Series: properties

Property or operation	Periodic signal	Discrete Fourier Series
Transformation	$x[n]$	$a_k = \dfrac{1}{N} \displaystyle\sum_{n=0}^{N-1} x[n] \exp(-j2\pi kn/N)$
Inverse transformation	$x[n] = \displaystyle\sum_{k=0}^{N-1} a_k \exp(j2\pi kn/N)$	a_k
Linearity	$Ax_1[n] + Bx_2[n]$	$Aa_k + Bb_k$
Time-shifting	$x[n - n_0]$	$a_k \exp(-j2\pi kn_0/N)$
Time-differentiation	$x[n] - x[n - 1]$	$a_k\{1 - \exp(-j2\pi k/N)\}$
Time-integration	$\displaystyle\sum_{k=-\infty}^{n} x[k].\ a_0 = 0$	$a_k\{1 - \exp(-j2\pi k/N)\}^{-1}$
Convolution	$\displaystyle\sum_{m=0}^{N-1} x_1[m]x_2[n - m]$	$Na_k\, b_k$
Modulation	$x_1[n]x_2[n]$	$\displaystyle\sum_{m=0}^{N-1} a_m\, b_{k-m}$
Real time function	$x[n]$	$a_k = a^*_{-k}$ $Re(a_k) = Re(a_{-k})$ $Im(a_k) = -Im(a_{-k})$

Table B.2 The Fourier Transform of aperiodic digital signals: properties and pairs

Property or operation	Aperiodic signal	Fourier Transform
Transformation	$x[n]$	$X(\Omega) = \sum_{n=-\infty}^{\infty} x[n] \exp(-j\Omega n)$
Inverse transformation	$x[n] = \dfrac{1}{2\pi} \displaystyle\int_{2\pi} X(\Omega) \exp(j\Omega n)\, d\Omega$	$X(\Omega)$
Linearity	$ax_1[n] + bx_2[n]$	$aX_1(\Omega) + bX_2(\Omega)$
Time-shifting	$x[n - n_0]$	$X(\Omega) \exp(-j\Omega n_0)$
Time-differentiation	$x[n] - x[n - 1]$	$X(\Omega) \{1 - \exp(-j\Omega)\}$
Convolution	$x_1[n] * x_2[n]$	$X_1(\Omega) X_2(\Omega)$
Modulation	$x_1[n]\, x_2[n]$	$\dfrac{1}{2\pi} \displaystyle\int_{2\pi} X_1(\lambda)\, X_2(\Omega - \lambda)\, d\lambda$

Waveform	Aperiodic signal x[n]	Spectrum X(Ω)
Unit impulse	$\delta[n]$	1
Shifted unit impulse	$\delta[n - n_0]$	$\exp(-j\Omega n_0)$
Unit step	$u[n]$	$\{1 - \exp(-j\Omega)\}^{-1}$ $+ \displaystyle\sum_{k=-\infty}^{\infty} \pi\, \delta(\Omega - 2\pi k)$
Exponential	$a^n u[n],\ |a| < 1$	$\{1 - a \exp(-j\Omega)\}^{-1}$
Rectangular pulse	$x[n] = 1,\ |n| \leq m$ $x[n] = 0,\ |n| > m$	$\dfrac{\sin\{(m + \frac{1}{2})\Omega\}}{\sin\left(\dfrac{\Omega}{2}\right)}$

Digital Signals, Processors and Noise

Table B.3 The unilateral z-Transform: pairs

Waveform	Signal x[n]	Spectrum X(z)	z-plane poles and zeros
Unit impulse	$\delta[n]$	1	Unit circle
Unit step	$u[n]$	$\dfrac{z}{(z-1)}$	
Unit ramp	$r[n]$	$\dfrac{z}{(z-1)^2}$	2nd order
Exponential	$a^n\, u[n]$	$\dfrac{z}{(z-a)}$	
	$(1-a^n)\, u[n]$	$\dfrac{z(1-a)}{(z-a)(z-1)}$	
Cosine	$\cos n\Omega_0\, u[n]$	$\dfrac{z(z-\cos \Omega_0)}{(z^2-2z\cos \Omega_0+1)}$	
Sine	$\sin n\Omega_0\, u[n]$	$\dfrac{z\sin \Omega_0}{(z^2-2z\cos \Omega_0+1)}$	
Damped sine	$a^n \sin n\Omega_0\, u[n]$	$\dfrac{az\sin \Omega_0}{(z^2-2az\cos \Omega_0+a^2)}$	

Table B.4   The unilateral z-Transform: properties

Property or operation	Signal	z-Transform
Transformation	$x[n]$	$\displaystyle\sum_{n=0}^{\infty} x[n]\, z^{-n}$
Inverse transformation	$\displaystyle\frac{1}{2\pi j} \oint X(z)\, z^{n-1}\, dz$	$X(z)$
Linearity	$a_1 x_1[n] + a_2 x_2[n]$	$a_1 X_1(z) + a_2 X_2(z)$
Time-shifting	$x[n - n_0]\, u[n - n_0]$	$X(z)\, z^{-n_0}$
Time-differentiation	$x(n) - x(n-1)$	$X(z)\,(1 - z^{-1})$
Time-integration	$\displaystyle\sum_{k=0}^{n} x[k]$	$X(z)\left(\dfrac{z}{z-1}\right)$
Convolution	$x_1[n] * x_2[n]$	$X_1(z)\, X_2(z)$
Final-value theorem	$\displaystyle\lim_{n\to\infty} x[n]$	$\displaystyle\lim_{z\to 1}\left(\dfrac{z-1}{z}\right) X(z)$

Table B.5   The Discrete Fourier Transform: properties

Property or operation	*Signal*	*DFT*
Transformation	$x[n]$	$X[k] = \sum_{n=0}^{N-1} x[n]\, W_N^{kn},$ $0 \leqslant k \leqslant (N-1)$
Inverse transformation	$x[n] = \dfrac{1}{N} \sum_{k=0}^{N-1} X[k]\, W_N^{-kn},$ $0 \leqslant n \leqslant (N-1)$	$X[k]$
Linearity	$Ax_1[n] + Bx_2[n]$	$AX_1[k] + BX_2[k]$
Time-shifting	$x[n - n_0]$	$X[k]\, W_N^{kn_0}$
Convolution	$\sum_{m=0}^{N-1} x_1[n]\, x_2[m - n]$	$X_1[k]\, X_2[k]$
Modulation	$x_1[n]\, x_2[n]$	$\dfrac{1}{N} \sum_{m=0}^{N-1} X_1[m]\, X_2[k - m]$
Real time function	$x[n]$	$X[k] = X^*[-k]$ $\Re(X[k]) = \Re(X[-k])$ $\Im(X[k]) = -\Im(X[-k])$

Answers to Selected Problems

Chapter 1

1.2. (a) Period $= 18$;   (d) period $= 20$

1.4. If $|\alpha| > 1$, system is unstable

1.6. (a) $x[n] = \delta[n] + 2\delta[n - 1] + \delta[n - 2]$

(b) $x[n] = 2\delta[n + 2] + 2\delta[n] - 0.5\delta[n - 1] + \delta[n - 4]$

1.7. (a), (c), (d) are causal and stable

1.9. (a) 2;   (b) 2/3

1.11. (a) $y[n] = \displaystyle\sum_{k=0}^{6} x[n - k]$

(b) $y[n] = \displaystyle\sum_{k=0}^{\infty} (0.9)^k x[n - k]$

1.12. Overall $h[n]$ has sample values (starting at $n = 1$): 1, 2.5, 4.333, 2.167, 1, 0, 0 . . .

1.13. (a) $a_0 = 5$, $a_1 = a_7 = 0.5$, $a_2 = -a_6 = -0.5$j, $a_3 = a_5 = 0$, $a_4 = 0$

(b) $a_1 = (1 - \text{j})/2\sqrt{2}$, $a_3 = (1 + \text{j})/2\sqrt{2}$

(c) $a_0 = 3$, $a_1 = -1 + \text{j}$, $a_2 = -1$, $a_3 = -1 -\text{j}$

1.15. 0.518, 75°

1.17. $H(\Omega) = \dfrac{0.1}{1 + 0.9\ \exp(-\text{j}\Omega)}$;   (a) 0.0526;   (b) 1.0

1.18. $|H(\Omega)| = \{(1 - 0.9\ \cos\Omega + 0.8\ \cos2\Omega)^2 + (0.9\ \sin\Omega - 0.8\ \sin2\Omega)^2\}^{-1/2}$

1.20. $Y(z) = (1 + 3z^{-1} + 6z^{-2} + 6z^{-3} + 3z^{-4} + z^{-5} + z^{-7})$

1.21. (a) $x[n] = \left(\dfrac{1}{\sqrt{2}}\right)^n \sin\dfrac{n\pi}{4} u[n]$

(b) $x[n] = \{2.5 - 1.5(0.8)^{n-2}\} u[n - 2]$

1.23. (a) Zeros at $z = 2$, $z = -1$

Poles at $z = 0.5$, $z = 0.8$

  (b) Zeros at $z = 0.5 \pm \text{j}0.866$
      Poles at $z = \pm\text{j}$
      Unstable
  (c) Zeros at $z = 1$, $z = \pm\text{j}$
      Poles at $z = \pm0.5$
      Non-causal
  (d) Nine zeros equally spaced around unit circle
      Pole at $z = 1$, eighth-order pole at origin
      Stable
1.24. (a) $x[n] = (1 - \alpha^{-0.8})\,u[n]$

  (b) $x[n] = \left(\cos\dfrac{2\pi n}{3}\right)u[n]$

  (c) $x[n] = \left(0.8^n \sin\dfrac{\pi n}{2}\right)u[n]$

1.26. $-2 < \alpha < 2$; $\beta < 1$
  (a) $\alpha = 1$;   (b) $\alpha = -1$

Chapter 2

2.2. Impulse response values $h[0]$ to $h[m]$ are:
  (a) 0.4, 0.30273, 0.09355, -0.06237, -0.07568 . . .
  (b) 0.2, -0.1870, 0.15137, -0.10091, 0.04677 . . .
2.3. Window values $w[0]$ to $w[m]$ are:
  (a) 1.0, 0.93301, 0.75, 0.5, 0.25, 0.06699
  (b) 1.0, 0.93837, 0.77, 0.54, 0.31, 0.14163, 0.08
2.4. 0.143 dB; 0.579 dB
2.6. $y[n] = 1.5164y[n-1] - 0.8783y[n-2] + x[n]$
         $-1.6180x[n-1] + x[n-2]$
2.8. (a) Polar coordinates of poles:
      $r = 0.32492$, $\theta = 0$
      $r = 0.83360$, $\theta = \pm53.31°$
      $r = 0.57395$, $\theta = \pm47.10°$
      $r = 0.39599$, $\theta = \pm30.85°$
      (also seventh-order zero at $z = -1$)
2.9. Sixth-order
2.10. Polar coordinates of poles:
      $r = 0.90985$, $\theta = 180°$
      $r = 0.95479$, $\theta = \pm163.71°$
      (also third-order zero at $z = 1$)
      Peak gain $= 1126.2$ (61.03 dB)

Cut-off at 0.8π is -29 dB

$$y[n] = -2.7428y[n - 1] - 2.5793y[n - 2]$$
$$-0.8294y[n - 3] + x[n] - 3x[n - 1]$$
$$+3x[n - 2] - x[n - 3]$$

2.11. $y[n] = 1.7236y[n - 1] - 0.74082y[n - 2]$
$$+ x[n] - 0.9909x[n - 1]$$

Chapter 3

3.2. (a) $3X[k]$

(b) $X[k] \, W_N^{2k}$

(c) $X[k] \, \{2 + W_N^{-k}\}$

(d) $\dfrac{1}{N} \displaystyle\sum_{m=0}^{N-1} X[m] \, X[k - m] \, W_N^{k-m}$

3.3. (a) $X[0] = 0$, $X[1] = 2$

(b) $7, j, -3, -j$

3.4. (a) $X[9]$ and $X[31]$

(b) $X[0] = X[39] = 0$

3.7. 0, 16, 8, 24, 4, 20, 12, 28, 2, 18, 10, 26, 6, 22, 14, 30, 1, 17, 9, 25, 5, 21, 13, 29, 3, 19, 11, 27, 7, 23, 15, 31

3.10. (a) 8th and 56th

(b) 7th and 57th; -6.56 dB

(c) 480 samples/second

3.11. (a) 21.48 Hz

(b) 0.0491 radian

(c) 0.00586 Hz

3.13. One period of circular convolution has values:

$$4, 1, -3, 1, 1, 0$$

Linear convolution gives values:

$$1, 1, -1, 0, 0, 0, 3, 0, -2, 1, 1$$

Chapter 4

4.1. (b) Mean $= 0$, mean-square $= 2/3$, variance $= 2/3$

4.2. (b) Mean $= 4$, mean-square $= 19$, variance $= 3$.

4.5. Mean $= 0.4$, mean-square $= 0.8$,
standard deviation $= 0.8$; ± 3 sampling intervals

4.7. (a) $\phi_{xx}[m] = \dfrac{\pi}{2} \operatorname{sinc}\left(\dfrac{\pi m}{4}\right)$

4.10. $1 + 2\exp(-j\Omega) + 2\exp(-j2\Omega) + \exp(-j3\Omega)$

Chapter 5

5.1. (a) 6
    (b) 0.5556
    (c) 2.857

5.2. $\dfrac{4}{1 - 2r\cos\theta + r^2}$

5.3. (a) 2
    (c) 10
    (d) $P_{yy}(\Omega) = 10 + 16\cos\Omega + 8\cos2\Omega + 2\cos3\Omega$
5.4. Variance = 8
5.5. (a) $H(\Omega) = 2 + \exp(-j\Omega) + \exp(-j2\Omega)$
5.7. (a) 10 dB
    (b) 17 dB
    (c) 16 dB
5.8. 7.96 Hz (approx.)
5.11. (a) 2.73 dB
    (c) 7.78 dB
5.12. (a) 100
    (b) 100 000

Bibliography

The books listed below represent a fairly comprehensive coverage of DSP and associated topics. Several of them, including nos. 1, 5, and 6, give a substantial list of research references and are therefore useful guides to further study.

General books on Digital Signal Processing (DSP)

1. Bellanger, M., *Digital Processing of Signals*, Wiley, Chichester, 2nd edn, 1989.
2. Defatta, D. J. and Lucas, J. I., *Digital Signal Processing*, Wiley, New York, 1988.
3. Ludeman, L. C., *Fundamentals of Digital Signal Processing*, Wiley, New York, 1986.
4. Lynn, P. A. and Fuerst, W., *Introductory Digital Signal Processing with Computer Applications*, Wiley, Chichester, 1989.
5. Oppenheim, A. V. and Schafer, R. W., *Digital Signal Processing*, Prentice-Hall, Englewood Cliffs, NJ, 1975.
6. Stanley, W. D., Dougherty, G. R. and Dougherty, R., *Digital Signal Processing*, Reston, Virginia, 1984.
7. Williams, C. S., *Designing Digital Filters*, Prentice-Hall, Englewood Cliffs, NJ, 1986.

More specialised books on DSP

8. Bowen, B. A. and Brown, W. R., *VLSI Systems Design for Digital Signal Processing. Vol. 1: Signal Processing and Signal Processors*, Prentice-Hall, Englewood Cliffs, NJ, 1982.
9. Burrus, C. S. and Parks, T. W., *DFT/FFT and Convolution Algorithms*, Wiley, New York, 1985.
10. Chassaing, R. and Horning, D. W., *Digital Signal Processing with the TMS320C25*, Wiley, New York, 1990.

11. Hamming, R. W., *Digital Filters*, Prentice-Hall, Englewood Cliffs, NJ, 2nd edn, 1983.
12. Kung, S. Y., Whitehouse, H. J. and Kailath, T., *VLSI and Modern Signal Processing*, Prentice-Hall, Englewood Cliffs, NJ, 1985.

Books covering analog, as well as digital, signals and systems

13. Baher, H., *Analog and Digital Signal Processing*, Wiley, Chichester, 1990.
14. Gabel, R. A. and Roberts, R. A., *Signals and Linear Systems*, Wiley, New York, 3rd edn, 1987.
15. Lynn, P. A., *Electronic Signals and Systems*, Macmillan, London, 1986.
16. Lynn, P. A., *Introduction to the Analysis and Processing of Signals*, Macmillan, London, 3rd edn, 1989.
17. Oppenheim, A. V., Willsky, A. S. and Young, I. T., *Signals and Systems*, Prentice-Hall, Englewood Cliffs, NJ, 1983.
18. Papoulis, A., *Probability, Random Variables, and Stochastic Processes*, McGraw-Hill, New York, 1965.
19. Schwartz, M., *Information Transmission, Modulation, and Noise*, McGraw-Hill, New York, 2nd edn, 1970.

Index